JUNIOR GREAT BOOKS

SERIES 4

FIRST SEMESTER

◆   ◆   ◆

AN INTERPRETIVE READING, WRITING,

AND DISCUSSION CURRICULUM

JUNIOR GREAT BOOKS

SERIES 4   FIRST SEMESTER

THE GREAT BOOKS FOUNDATION
A nonprofit educational corporation

First Printing

9   8   7   6   5   4   3   2

Printed in the United States of America

Published and distributed by

THE GREAT BOOKS FOUNDATION
A nonprofit educational corporation

35 East Wacker Drive, Suite 2300

Chicago, IL 60601-2298

CONTENTS

It was about eleven o'clock at night.

THANK YOU, M'AM

Langston Hughes

She was a large woman with a large purse that had everything in it but a hammer and nails. It had a long strap, and she carried it slung across her shoulder. It was about eleven o'clock at night, dark, and she was walking alone, when a boy ran up behind her and tried to snatch her purse. The strap broke with the sudden single tug the boy gave it from behind. But the boy's weight and the weight of the purse combined caused him to lose his balance. Instead of taking off full blast as he had hoped, the boy fell on his back on the sidewalk and his legs flew up. The large woman simply turned around and kicked him right square in his blue-jeaned sitter. Then she reached down, picked the boy up by his shirt front, and shook him until his teeth rattled.

After that the woman said, "Pick up my pocketbook, boy, and give it here."

She still held him tightly. But she bent down enough to permit him to stoop and pick up her purse. Then she said, "Now ain't you ashamed of yourself?"

Firmly gripped by his shirt front, the boy said, "Yes'm."

The woman said, "What did you want to do it for?"

The boy said, "I didn't aim to."

She said, "You a lie!"

By that time two or three people passed, stopped, turned to look, and some stood watching.

"If I turn you loose, will you run?" asked the woman.

"Yes'm," said the boy.

"Then I won't turn you loose," said the woman. She did not release him.

"Lady, I'm sorry," whispered the boy.

"Um-hum! Your face is dirty. I got a great mind to wash your face for you. Ain't you got nobody home to tell you to wash your face?"

"No'm," said the boy.

"Then it will get washed this evening," said the large woman, starting up the street, dragging the frightened boy behind her.

He looked as if he were fourteen or fifteen, frail and willow-wild, in tennis shoes and blue jeans.

The woman said, "You ought to be my son. I would teach you right from wrong. Least I can do right now is to wash your face. Are you hungry?"

"No'm," said the being-dragged boy. "I just want you to turn me loose."

"Was I bothering *you* when I turned that corner?" asked the woman.

"No'm."

"But you put yourself in contact with *me*," said the woman. "If you think that that contact is not going to last awhile, you got another thought coming. When I get through with you, sir, you are going to remember Mrs. Luella Bates Washington Jones."

Sweat popped out on the boy's face and he began to struggle. Mrs. Jones stopped, jerked him around in front of her, put a half nelson about his neck, and continued to drag him up the street. When she got to her door, she dragged the boy inside, down a hall, and into a large kitchenette-furnished room at the rear of the house. She switched on the light and left the door open. The boy could hear other roomers laughing and talking in the large house. Some of their doors were open, too, so he knew he and the woman were not alone. The woman still had him by the neck in the middle of her room.

She said, "What is your name?"

"Roger," answered the boy.

"Then, Roger, you go to that sink and wash your face," said the woman, whereupon she turned him loose—at last. Roger looked at the door—looked at the woman—looked at the door—*and went to the sink.*

"Let the water run until it gets warm," she said. "Here's a clean towel."

"You gonna take me to jail?" asked the boy, bending over the sink.

"Not with that face, I would not take you nowhere," said the woman. "Here I am trying to get home to cook me a bite to eat, and you snatch my pocketbook! Maybe you ain't been to your supper either, late as it be. Have you?"

"There's nobody home at my house," said the boy.

"Then we'll eat," said the woman. "I believe you're hungry—or been hungry—to try to snatch my pocketbook!"

"I want a pair of blue suede shoes," said the boy.

"Well, you didn't have to snatch *my* pocketbook to get some suede shoes," said Mrs. Luella Bates Washington Jones. "You could of asked me."

"M'am?"

The water dripping from his face, the boy looked at her. There was a long pause. A very long pause. After he had dried his face and not knowing what else to do, dried it again, the boy turned around, wondering what next. The door was open. He could make a dash for it down the hall. He could run, run, run, *run*!

The woman was sitting on the daybed. After a while she said, "I were young once and I wanted things I could not get."

There was another long pause. The boy's mouth opened. Then he frowned, not knowing he frowned.

The woman said, "Um-hum! You thought I was going to say *but,* didn't you? You thought I was going to say, *but I didn't snatch people's pocketbooks.* Well, I wasn't going to say that." Pause. Silence. "I have done things, too, which I would not tell you, son—neither tell God, if He didn't already know. Everybody's got something in common. So you set down while I fix us something to eat. You might run that comb through your hair so you will look presentable."

In another corner of the room behind a screen was a gas plate and an icebox. Mrs. Jones got up and went behind the screen. The woman did not watch the boy to see if he was going to run now, nor did she watch her purse, which she left behind her on the daybed. But the boy took care to sit on the far side of the room, away from the purse, where he thought she could easily see him out of the corner of her eye if she wanted to. He did not trust the woman *not* to trust him. And he did not want to be mistrusted now.

13

"Do you need somebody to go to the store," asked the boy, "maybe to get some milk or something?"

"Don't believe I do," said the woman, "unless you just want sweet milk yourself. I was going to make cocoa out of this canned milk I got here."

"That will be fine," said the boy.

She heated some lima beans and ham she had in the icebox, made the cocoa, and set the table. The woman did not ask the boy anything about where he lived, or his folks, or anything else that would embarrass him. Instead, as they ate, she told him about her job in a hotel beauty shop that stayed open late, what the work was like, and how all kinds of women came in and out, blondes, redheads, and Spanish. Then she cut him a half of her ten-cent cake.

"Eat some more, son," she said.

When they were finished eating, she got up and said, "Now here, take this ten dollars and buy yourself some blue suede shoes. And next time, do not make the mistake of latching onto *my* pocketbook *nor nobody else's*—because shoes got by devilish ways will burn your feet. I got to get my rest now. But from here on in, son, I hope you will behave yourself."

She led him down the hall to the front door and opened it. "Good night! Behave yourself, boy!" she said, looking out into the street as he went down the steps.

The boy wanted to say something other than, "Thank you, m'am," to Mrs. Luella Bates Washington Jones, but although his lips moved, he couldn't even say that as he turned at the foot of the barren stoop and looked up at the large woman in the door. Then she shut the door.

He shook the water from his magnificent black mane.

THE WATER-HORSE OF BARRA

Scottish folktale
as told by Winifred Finlay

Once upon a time there lived a water-horse on the island of Barra in the Outer Hebrides, which lie off the west coast of Scotland.

Now a water-horse, people believed, had magic powers, so that he could live happily in his home at the bottom of a loch, but when he swam up to the surface and reached dry land, then he could gallop about as an ordinary horse, or he could change himself into a man, just as he pleased.

This water-horse was a magnificent black creature with long legs, brown eyes, and a splendid flowing mane, and because he was very good-natured and never caused anyone any harm, he got on well with the fairies who lived in a nearby hill, and with the humans who lived in a hamlet not far away, and earned a living by farming and fishing.

After several hundred years, however, the water-horse began to feel lonely. The fairies had moved from their underground home because people no longer believed in them, and whenever he changed himself into a young man, human beings did not seem to be as friendly as they once had been, saying that they had no time to sit and talk with him because they had to see to the milking, or start ploughing, or set snares for rabbits, or search for bait, or put the children to bed.

"What I need is a wife," the water-horse thought. "Every morning I'll catch fresh fish for breakfast, and in case she does not like raw fish as I do, I shall build a fireplace and a chimney in my house at the bottom of the loch, and she can sit in front of it and cook meals on it, just as all humans do."

Rising to the surface of the loch, he shook the water from his magnificent black mane, and galloped off through the reeds and right across the island, looking to right and to left in search of a suitable wife.

There were not many girls on Barra and each one seemed to have something wrong with her, from the water-horse's point of view. This one was too fat and so would be lazy, that one too thin and would eat too much. Another was too tall, a fourth too small, and a fifth so ugly that the water-horse knew he could never bear to see her face every morning across the breakfast table. He was, you see, a very particular water-horse, and having lived alone for so many hundred years, he had grown rather selfish, so that never for one moment did he consider what the girls might think of him.

Just when he was on the point of giving up hope of ever finding a bride to please him, he saw a girl sitting in the heather, watching over her father's cows, and knitting industriously. Around her the bees murmured softly as they searched for honey, forming a pleasant musical background to the busy click clack of the needles.

This girl was neither too fat nor too thin, too tall nor too small and she had grey eyes that were made for laughing and a red mouth that was made for smiling, so that the water-horse fell in love with her immediately, and knew that he had found just the kind of wife he wanted.

Never stopping to consider what ideas on the subject the girl might have, he galloped across to her, whinnied, and tossed his magnificent black mane.

"What a splendid creature you are," the girl said, and putting down her knitting, she stood up and began to stroke the neck of the water-horse and then, to her dismay, found that she could not take her hand away.

Because she was clever as well as being pretty, she realised immediately that this was no ordinary horse, and that by touching it, she had put herself in its power.

19

"You are the prettiest girl in Barra," the water-horse said. "Your eyes are as grey as the waters of my loch in midwinter, your hair as yellow as the sands on the shore, and your skin as white as the waterlilies which unfold their buds every summer. I have, therefore, decided to make you my wife."

"How kind of you," the girl answered politely, knowing that she would need to have her wits about her to free herself from the magic of the water-horse. "However, if I am to live at the bottom of a loch for the rest of my life, I hope you won't mind if I just finish knitting these socks to keep my feet warm."

"Of course not," the water-horse said, equally politely.

"Sit down in the heather beside me, and rest a little in the sunshine, while I turn this heel," the girl said.

Immediately the water-horse changed himself into a handsome young man with hair as black as the raven's wing, and brown eyes which were strangely cold and selfish from living alone for hundreds of years.

"Help me, bees," the girl murmured, as the young man sat down in the heather beside her, and because the bees knew that it was she who gave them a home in the hard days of winter, they flew backwards and forwards, singing drowsily of the hot sunshine and the scent of the heather and the softly nodding heads of the harebells so that all the young man wanted was to fall asleep there and then.

When he had yawned for the third time, the girl said:

"Yours must be a very busy and strenuous life. While I am finishing this foot, why don't you stretch out in the heather and sleep a little?"

"What a good idea," the young man said, and the next moment he was sound asleep in the sunshine, and having done what the girl had asked them, the bees flew off on their search for yet more honey.

"He really is extremely handsome," the girl thought, looking down at the sleeping young man, "but I have no intention of marrying a water-horse and spending the rest of my life at the bottom of a loch," and she beckoned to the nearest of her father's cows.

"Help me, cow," she whispered, and because the cow knew that it was she who watched over them in the daytime, and milked them every morning and evening, she bent her head.

"Take the rope halter from my neck," the cow said, "and place it over the head of the young man. He will then change back into a water-horse, and be in your power as long as the halter is there."

Taking the halter from the cow's neck, the girl placed it over the head of the sleeping young man. Immediately he awoke and changed back into a water-horse, but because he now was in her power, he could no longer speak, and could only look at her with sad, rather selfish brown eyes.

"And now you must learn your lesson, water-horse," the girl said. "It may have been all right to carry off a girl and marry her when you first came to live in the loch, but things have changed a great deal since those days."

She led the water-horse off to her father's farm.

"I have brought you the best horse you have ever seen, or ever are likely to see, to work for you," she said. "But remember this. Never take off the cow halter from his neck, no matter how sadly he may look at you. And now you must bring in the cows yourself and milk them, because I am off to consult the Wise Man of Barra, and with your permission I shall take him the bowl of crowdie which I made yesterday."

Wrapping the bowl of cream cheese carefully in a clean cloth, she set off to consult the Wise Man, who had the Sight and could foretell what the future held.

"There is nothing to be done now," the Wise Man said. "Bring the water-horse to me when you hear the cuckoo sing over Barra and I'll see what can be done then." And he grabbed the crowdie and shut the door firmly in her face.

Rather sadly—because it was many years since the cuckoo had been heard over Barra—the girl returned to her farm and her work there, and if she was not particularly happy, her father certainly was, because the water-horse did the work of seven ordinary horses and ate hardly anything at all.

"In seven years this horse will have made my fortune," he rejoiced, "and then I shall take him to the horse market at Castlebay and sell him for a good sum."

But the girl had other ideas. To a water-horse, seven years might seem like only one day, but to her they were a very long time, and anyway she had no intention of allowing her father to sell the creature.

Every night, when the horse had finished working on the farm and was tied up by the cow halter in its stable, she would go down and feed and groom him, and as she brushed his long, black mane, she would talk to him of all the work which had been done that day on the farm and of all that they were planning to do. Sometimes she would sing to him songs that the island women sang as they spun and wove, as they churned the butter and made the cheese, or as they rocked their babies to sleep; and all the time she was with him, the water-horse would listen attentively and stare at her with brown eyes which, little by little, grew less cold and less selfish.

Exactly a year and a day after the water-horse had gone in search of a wife, the girl heard the cuckoo singing over the island and she knew then that the time had come. Again she fed and groomed the horse, but this night she led him out of the stable and, holding the cow halter in one hand, mounted his back and rode him to the Wise Man, taking with her a bag of fine oatmeal of her own grinding.

"Take off the cow harness," the Wise Man commanded, as he opened his door to her knocking.

"But then we shall be in his power," the girl said.

"Take off the cow harness," the Wise Man repeated, having looked into the brown eyes of the water-horse and having seen what he had seen.

Nervously the girl took off the cow harness and immediately the water-horse changed into a young man—taller and stronger than he had been before, because of all the hard work he had done for the girl's father. His hair was as black as the raven's wing, his skin burned brown by the sun and the wind, and his eyes, which once had been so cold and selfish, now were full of love and entreaty.

"What have you to say to me?" the Wise Man asked the young man.

"A year and a day ago I wished to carry off this girl and make her my wife," the young man said. "Since then she has talked to me of her father's farm, and I myself have worked long hours there. I have learned how very different her life is from mine, and now I know that never could she be happy in my home at the bottom of the loch.

"When the fairies left Barra, I should have gone too, for now, alas! there is no place for either fairies or water-horses in the Western Islands."

24

"If you have learned that, you have learned much," the Wise Man said. "Supposing you had gone away with the fairies, what place would you have gone to?"

"Tir-nan-Og, the Land of Youth, where no one is unhappy and no one grows old," the young man answered.

"You are still free to go to Tir-nan-Og," the Wise Man reminded him, and then, as the young man hesitated, continued, "or you can give up the magic of the old gods and become a man, to love like one and grow old like one."

"How is that possible?" the young man asked.

"Drink this potion which I have brewed from honey and the juices of seven times seven herbs, all gathered when the old moon held the new moon in her arms. For twenty-four hours you will sleep, and when you awaken, the magic will have gone and you will be only a man."

The young man turned to the girl.

"Your eyes are as grey as the waters of my loch in midwinter," he said. "Your hair is as yellow as the sands on the shore, your skin as white as the water-lilies which unfold their buds every summer. If I became a man, would you marry me?"

"Gladly," the girl answered, knowing that the water-horse had learned his lesson, that his love was so great that he would give up his place in Tir-nan-Og to stay on Barra and marry her.

Taking the potion from the Wise Man, the young man drank it in a single gulp, and immediately fell into a deep sleep, and for twenty-four hours the girl sat by his side, watching over him, while the magic drained out of him. When he awoke he was a human being and had no recollection of ever being a water-horse or living at the bottom of the loch.

Now, while the farmer grieved at the loss of his remarkable horse, he rejoiced that his daughter had found herself such a strong and handsome husband who was prepared to work from dawn till dusk, and longer, if need be, and so he set the pair of them up in a farm on the far side of the island, and there they lived happily for many a long year, and for all I know, some of their grandchildren, or great-grandchildren, or great-great-grandchildren may be living there still.

He beheld a most beautiful sight.

THE STORY OF WANG LI

Elizabeth Coatsworth

Once in China many many years ago there lived a young man named Wang Li, with his old mother, on a small farm under the shadow of the Hill of the Seven Stars. When he was a boy he studied letters and charms with a famous sage who lived by himself in the Wind Cave halfway up the mountain. But when he had studied for several years he declared one morning that he would climb the rough path no more.

His mother was in despair.

"How hard have I labored without your help in the fields!" she cried. "Why, in a few years you could have called the cranes out of the sky to carry us anywhere we wished, or turned flower petals into money to buy whatever we desired! Ungrateful son! Return to your studies!"

But Wang Li only shook his head.

"I have learned all that I need," he replied. *"A big heart is better than a big house."*

Upon hearing a proverb quoted at her, Wang Li's mother grew furious, and seizing her broom, beat Wang Li over the shoulders until she was tired. He, being a filial son in most matters, waited until she had stopped, and then brought her a drink of cold water fresh from the well.

After that Wang Li helped his mother in the fields, but often he slipped away to the forests at the foot of the Hill of the Seven Stars with his bow and arrow, to wander in their green shades and perhaps bring back a hare for their dinner, until he became as expert a hunter as there was in the countryside.

So the days went by and at last there came a dry spring. Week after week passed and still no rain fell and the young rice and millet shoots stood small and yellow in the fields, and the mulberry leaves hung withered on the trees, unfit for the silkworms, and the melon vines lay brittle as straws on the baked ground. Prayers were said all day long in the Temple of the God of the Soil. Incense burned in great twisted ropes of sweetness about his nostrils, gongs were sounded before him, and offerings of fish and chickens and pork lay heaped on his altars.

But still no rain fell.

Early one morning Wang Li was wandering in the
forest when he saw something above his head that
looked like a flight of great swans, slowly settling down
towards the clear waters of Heaven Mirror Lake.
Creeping without sound through the underbrush, he at
last came to a thicket at the very edge of the water, and
parting the leaves with careful hands, he beheld a most
beautiful sight. The creatures whom he had seen were
not swans but winged maidens who were playing about
on the surface, splashing the water until it shone like the
crystal beads in their elaborate headdresses, shaking their
white wings with a sound like music, clapping their
delicate hands, and pursuing one another in sport.

It happened that during their games the most
beautiful of the damsels passed close to the thicket
where Wang Li was hidden. Swift as a hawk he seized
one snow-white wing in his strong hand, and while the
other maidens rose screaming into the air, he drew his
lovely captive to the shore.

For a little while she wept, but glancing at him
through her lashes, she was reassured and ceased to sob.
Still holding the edge of one bright wing, he questioned
her.

"What is your name, beautiful one?" he asked.

"I am called the Sky Damsel and am the youngest
daughter of the Cloud Dragon," she answered timidly.
And then went on: "You are the first human being

31

I have ever seen. If you will come with me I will take you to the sixteen palaces of my father that are built upon the clouds. One palace is of white jade and silver, and butterflies guard the gates; another palace is built of marble inlaid with rose quartz, and its gardens are famous for their peonies; another palace has walls of gold, and is overlooked by a high pagoda on which stands the bird of the sun to crow to the dawn; and the last palace is built of ebony with pavilions of scarlet lacquer, and Lightning stands on the left of the gate and Thunder on the right. If you will come, you shall be my husband and live in whichever palace you please, and you shall ride on steeds of vapor and pluck the stars as you pass."

"I am a poor man," said Wang Li, "and the son of a poor man. How should I live in a palace? But if I give you your freedom, Sky Damsel, will you swear to me that in return you will ask your august parent to send upon this unfortunate countryside the requisite rains, so that the crops shall flourish and the people may not die? And he might keep a special eye on my mother's little farm at the foot of Seven Stars Hill," he added, "for she works hard and likes her garden to do well."

"It shall be as you have said," replied the Sky Damsel, and she flew away, often looking back and weeping.

But Wang Li returned home, and as he neared his mother's house the rain began to fall, soft and warm, filling all the ditches with the gurgle of running water.

"Rejoice," cried his mother as he entered, "the drought is over! And just in time, too! Now the crops will be spared. I wonder how it occurred?"

"Oh, I know all about *that*," said Wang Li, and he told her what had happened by the lonely shore of Heaven Mirror Lake.

At once his mother flew into a rage.

"And you only asked for rain," she screamed, "when we might have lived in palaces, and worn silk woven from moonlight, and fed on the fruit of the immortals! Oh, you undutiful son!"

And she fell to beating him with her broom. But when at last she stopped, exhausted, he only remarked: *"A chicken coop is still a chicken coop even when covered with cloth of gold."* And he lifted a pot of dumplings which was in danger of boiling over.

Now the next year it happened that Roving Horse River was in flood, spreading out over its banks, ruining fields, and carrying away houses. Its waters came up nearly to the door of the cottage where Wang Li and his mother lived, and threatened her mulberry trees. She was in despair and wept bitterly, but Wang Li took his bow and arrow from the wall.

"Are you going hunting at such a time?" she screamed. "Oh, that I should have borne a son with no heart!"

But he only said: *"If you know how, a thing is not hard; if it is hard, then you don't know how."* And he left her with her mouth open, not understanding what he meant.

"I wish that boy would stop quoting proverbs," she muttered to herself. "He is as clever a boy as ever breathed, but what good does it do us?"

Meantime Wang Li walked along beside the bank of the river. And he saw the flood coming down in a great white wave. And having very keen eyes he saw in the midst of the wave a youth and a maiden, clothed in garments of white silk, riding white horses with silver bits. And attendants on white horses followed them.

Then Wang Li drew his bow, fitted an arrow into the string, and let it fly straight into the heart of the young man, who fell dead from his horse. At that the others turned their horses and rode away at full speed, and the flood receded with them.

But as they rode, Wang Li sent another arrow after them which pierced the high headdress of the noble lady and shone there like a long ornament. And after a few paces, she reined in her horse and slowly rode back to where Wang Li stood.

"Here is your arrow," she said, giving it to him. "I suppose I should thank you for not sending it through my heart as you did through my cousin's, the Prince of Roving Horse River."

"I could never do anything so discourteous," murmured Wang Li.

The lady regarded him for a long time.

"Since you have spared my person," she said, "I suppose it should be yours. If you will come with me you shall be my husband, and reign in the palaces of the River Dragons. You shall sit on a throne of coral in halls of jade and crystal, and the River Maidens shall dance before you the Dance of the Ripples, and the River Warriors shall dance to please you the Dance of the Tempest."

"And what will happen to the countryside while they dance?" asked Wang Li. "No, no, I am a poor man and the son of a poor man. What should I do in palaces? If you wish to show your gratitude, make me a pledge that the river shall hereafter stay within its banks, and perhaps you might be especially careful along the edge of my mother's farm, for she is a poor woman and it grieves her to see her work washed away."

The lady raised her hand in agreement, and turned her horse and rode off. But before she disappeared forever, she looked back for a last glimpse of Wang Li, and he saw that she was weeping. A little sad, he returned to his mother's house and, as he walked, he noticed how the waters were draining off the land, leaving behind them, as tribute, pools filled with round-mouthed fish.

His mother met him at the door.

"See! see!" she cried. "The waters are withdrawing! But you, you wicked son, you left me here to drown and little you cared!"

"Indeed, I only went to bring you help!" said Wang Li, and he told his mother all that had happened. At hearing the story she nearly choked with rage.

"What! We might have lived in river palaces and dined off turtle eggs and carps' tongues every day!" she cried. "And I might have ridden on a dragon forty feet long when I went calling! All this might have been mine but you refused it, you ungrateful son!" And she seized her broom.

Whack!

"Take that!"

Whack!

"And that!"

Whack! Whack! Whack!

"And that! and that! and that!"

But when at last her arm fell, Wang Li politely helped her to her chair and brought her a fan.

"Peace in a thatched hut—that is happiness," he said, once more quoting an old proverb.

"Be off with you!" replied his mother. "You are a wicked, ungrateful son and have no right to be using the words of wise men. Besides, they hadn't been offered palaces, I'm sure."

So the months passed and the rain fell when it was needed, and the river remained within its banks and reflected on its smooth waters the sun by day and the moon by night. But after some time the country was greatly disturbed by earthquakes. People were awakened from their sleep by the tremblings of their beds, the dishes danced on the tables, sheds fell flat to the earth, and everyone waited with horror for the final quake that should bring their roofs down about their heads.

"Now," wept Wang Li's old mother, "I shall die a violent death, I who might have slept safe beside the Silver Stream of Heaven or walked in the gardens of the river, if it had not been for this great foolish son."

But Wang Li took his spear and went to the mouth of the Cave of the Evening Sun which is on the west side of the Hill of the Seven Stars. Then he looked carefully at the ground beneath his feet, which was rounded up as though a huge mole had passed under it, and choosing a certain spot, drove his spear deep into the loosened soil.

"Whoever walks along that path again will scratch his back," he said to himself with satisfaction, and was about to return home when he noticed a beautiful girl who sat beside a rock spinning, and weeping as she spun.

"Why do you scatter the pearls of your eyes, young maiden?" asked Wang Li gently. And she, raising her tear-wet eyes to him, said:

"Alas, I am Precious Jade, the only daughter of the former Dragon King of the Mountains. But my ungrateful uncle has risen against his elder brother and imprisoned him in the innermost prison of the hills, and he has driven me out to work with unaccustomed hands, living in this coarse robe, and eating roots and berries, and sleeping under the stars."

Wang Li looked at her in her rough brown garments, and her beauty seemed like a flower bursting from its sheath.

"I think I have stopped the path of your uncle who has been disturbing us with his wanderings, and now perhaps he will stay in his cavern palaces. But for you I can do nothing, I fear, though I would gladly serve you."

At that Precious Jade looked at him shyly.

"If you would deign to take me away with you and allow me to serve your mother with my poor strength, I should no longer weep alone on this desolate mountain," she whispered.

"And what gifts would you bring my mother if I took you home as a bride?" asked Wang Li.

Then Precious Jade wrung her hands. "Alas," she said, "I have no gifts but only my will to serve you both." And she wept very bitterly.

At that Wang Li laughed and lifted her up in his arms and carried her home to his mother.

"Mercy!" cried the old woman. "Whom have we here?"

"It is Precious Jade, the daughter of the former Dragon King of the Mountains," said Wang Li, "and she has returned here to be your daughter-in-law."

The old woman was all in a flutter.

"I must have an hour to get ready before I can present myself at court. How many guests will there be at the feast, my little dove? And how many rooms shall I have in the palace? And what color are the lanterns, or does light shine from the gems themselves in the Kingdom of the Mountain Dragons?"

"Alas!" said Precious Jade. "My father is a prisoner and I am only an exile."

"Pshaw!" exclaimed the old woman. "What a daughter-in-law for you to bring back, you senseless oaf! Look at the robe she is wearing, and her hands are fit for nothing! Go and bring me a pail of water, you useless girl! As for you," she cried, turning to her son, "you shall feel if my old arms are withered yet!" And she caught up her broom and began belaboring him with it.

A thin horse has long hair," remarked Wang Li philosophically when she had done, and he went out into the garden to find her a peach to refresh her after so much effort.

"I shall have to make the best of it," she grumbled to herself, when she had eaten the peach. "The boy has ears of stone. He follows his own way. *If the mountain will not turn, I must be the road and do the turning myself.*" After that she was kind to Precious Jade, who tried to be of help to her mother-in-law in every possible way.

So they lived together in peace and happiness, working hard, incurring no debts, and showing kindness to all. Throughout the district the rains fell punctually, no one had any complaint of Roving Horse River, and the earth was no longer shaken by the burrowing of dragons. In time Precious Jade bore a beautiful son whom they named Little Splendor and there were never four happier people in the world. One day, not long afterwards, as Wang Li and Precious Jade sat alone beneath a grapevine trellis which Wang Li had recently made, Precious Jade began, laying down her embroidery:

"My dear husband, a message has reached me from my father. It seems that my unworthy uncle, issuing forth hastily from his palace, struck himself against the point of your spear and after some time died. My father is again on his jewel throne, and naturally feels a deep gratitude towards you." She paused.

"Now you are going to tell me about the palaces under the mountains which I may have for the asking," said Wang Li.

"I always hated palaces. There was never anything to do," said Precious Jade, smiling. Then she went back to her embroidery.

"My husband is the proudest man in the world," she remarked to a yellow silk butterfly which she had not quite finished.

"Proud?" asked Wang Li. "Yet here I am and I might be a prince."

"You're too proud to be a prince," she replied, "and that is why I love you. I always wanted to marry the proudest man in the world."

"Maybe it's pride and maybe it's wisdom," said Wang Li, "but there are palaces and terraces of the mind I would not exchange for all the riches of the dragons."

And Precious Jade understood. In time Wang Li became so famous for his wisdom and benevolence that sages traveled from the farthest provinces to walk with him as he followed his plow. But sometimes when he was busy and the old mother needed a new silk gown or the baby wanted sweetmeats, Precious Jade would softly shake the leaves of the tree beside the door, and down would fall a light shower of silver coins. And Wang Li never noticed what it was that Precious Jade gathered under the mulberry tree.

This is the Elephant's Child having his nose pulled by the Crocodile. He is much surprised and astonished and hurt, and he is talking through his nose and saying, "Led go! You are hurtig be!" He is pulling very hard, and so is the Crocodile; but the Bi-Coloured-Python-Rock-Snake is hurrying through the water to help the Elephant's Child. All that black stuff is the banks of the great grey-green, greasy Limpopo River (but I am not allowed to paint these pictures), and the bottly-tree with the twisty roots and the eight leaves is one of the fever-trees that grow there.

    Underneath the truly picture are shadows of African animals walking into an African ark. There are two lions, two ostriches, two oxen, two camels, two sheep, and two other things that look like rats, but I think they are rock-rabbits. They don't mean anything. I put them in because I thought they looked pretty. They would look very fine if I were allowed to paint them.   —R.K.

THE ELEPHANT'S CHILD

Rudyard Kipling

In the High and Far-Off Times the Elephant, O Best Beloved, had no trunk. He had only a blackish, bulgy nose, as big as a boot, that he could wriggle about from side to side; but he couldn't pick up things with it. But there was one Elephant—a new Elephant—an Elephant's Child—who was full of 'satiable curtiosity, and that means he asked ever so many questions. *And* he lived in Africa, and he filled all Africa with his 'satiable curtiosities. He asked his tall aunt, the Ostrich, why her tail-feathers grew just so, and his tall aunt, the Ostrich, spanked him with her hard, hard claw. He asked his tall uncle, the Giraffe, what made his skin spotty, and his tall uncle, the Giraffe, spanked him with his hard, hard hoof. And still he was full of

43

'satiable curtiosity! He asked his broad aunt, the Hippopotamus, why her eyes were red, and his broad aunt, the Hippopotamus, spanked him with her broad, broad hoof; and he asked his hairy uncle, the Baboon, why melons tasted just so, and his hairy uncle, the Baboon, spanked him with his hairy, hairy paw. And *still* he was full of 'satiable curtiosity! He asked questions about everything that he saw, or heard, or felt, or smelt, or touched, and all his uncles and his aunts spanked him. And still he was full of 'satiable curtiosity!

One fine morning in the middle of the Precession of the Equinoxes this 'satiable Elephant's Child asked a new fine question that he had never asked before. He asked, "What does the Crocodile have for dinner?" Then everybody said, "Hush!" in a loud and dretful tone, and they spanked him immediately and directly, without stopping, for a long time.

By and by, when that was finished, he came upon Kolokolo Bird sitting in the middle of a wait-a-bit thorn bush, and he said, "My father has spanked me, and my mother has spanked me; all my aunts and uncles have spanked me for my 'satiable curtiosity; and *still* I want to know what the Crocodile has for dinner!"

Then Kolokolo Bird said, with a mournful cry, "Go to the banks of the great grey-green, greasy Limpopo River, all set about with fever-trees, and find out."

That very next morning, when there was nothing left of the Equinoxes, because the Precession had preceded according to precedent, this 'satiable Elephant's Child took a hundred pounds of bananas (the little short red kind), and a hundred pounds of sugar cane (the long purple kind), and seventeen melons (the greeny-crackly kind), and said to all his dear families, "Goodbye. I am going to the great grey-green, greasy Limpopo River, all set about with fever-trees, to find out what the Crocodile has for dinner." And they all spanked him once more for luck, though he asked them most politely to stop.

Then he went away, a little warm, but not at all astonished, eating melons, and throwing the rind about, because he could not pick it up.

He went from Graham's Town to Kimberley, and from Kimberley to Khama's Country, and from Khama's Country he went east by north, eating melons all the time, till at last he came to the banks of the great grey-green, greasy Limpopo River, all set about with fever-trees, precisely as Kolokolo Bird had said.

Now you must know and understand, O Best Beloved, that till that very week and day, and hour, and minute, this 'satiable Elephant's Child had never seen a Crocodile and did not know what one was like. It was all his 'satiable curtiosity.

The first thing that he found was a Bi-Coloured-Python-Rock-Snake curled round a rock.

" 'Scuse me," said the Elephant's Child most politely, "but have you seen such a thing as a Crocodile in these promiscuous parts?"

"*Have* I seen a Crocodile?" said the Bi-Coloured-Python-Rock-Snake, in a voice of dretful scorn. "What will you ask me next?"

" 'Scuse me," said the Elephant's Child, "but could you kindly tell me what he has for dinner?"

Then the Bi-Coloured-Python-Rock-Snake uncoiled himself very quickly from the rock and spanked the Elephant's Child with his scalesome, flailsome tail.

"That is odd," said the Elephant's Child, "because my father and my mother, and my uncle and my aunt, not to mention my other aunt, the Hippopotamus, and my other uncle, the Baboon, have all spanked me for my 'satiable curtiosity—and I suppose this is the same thing."

So he said goodbye very politely to the Bi-Coloured-Python-Rock-Snake, and helped to coil him up on the rock again, and went on, a little warm, but not at all astonished, eating melons, and throwing the rind about, because he could not pick it up, till he trod on what he thought was a log of wood at the very edge of the great grey-green, greasy Limpopo River, all set about with fever-trees.

But it was really the Crocodile, O Best Beloved, and the Crocodile winked one eye—like this!

" 'Scuse me," said the Elephant's Child most politely, "but do you happen to have seen a Crocodile in these promiscuous parts?"

Then the Crocodile winked the other eye, and lifted half his tail out of the mud; and the Elephant's Child stepped back most politely, because he did not wish to be spanked again.

"Come hither, Little One," said the Crocodile. "Why do you ask such things?"

" 'Scuse me," said the Elephant's Child, most politely, "but my father has spanked me, my mother has spanked me, not to mention my tall aunt, the Ostrich, and my tall uncle, the Giraffe, who can kick ever so hard, as well as my broad aunt, the Hippopotamus, and my hairy uncle, the Baboon, *and* including the Bi-Coloured-Python-Rock-Snake, with the scalesome, flailsome tail, just up the bank, who spanks harder than any of them; and *so,* if it's quite all the same to you, I don't want to be spanked any more."

"Come hither, Little One," said the Crocodile, "for I am the Crocodile," and he wept crocodile-tears to show it was quite true.

Then the Elephant's Child grew all breathless, and panted, and kneeled down on the bank and said, "You are the very person I have been looking for all these long days. Will you please tell me what you have for dinner?"

"Come hither, Little One," said the Crocodile, "and I'll whisper."

Then the Elephant's Child put his head down close to the Crocodile's musky, tusky mouth, and the Crocodile caught him by his little nose, which up to that very week, day, hour, and minute, had been no bigger than a boot, though much more useful.

"I think," said the Crocodile—and he said it between his teeth, like this—"I think today I will begin with Elephant's Child!"

At this, O Best Beloved, the Elephant's Child was much annoyed, and he said, speaking through his nose, like this, "Led go! You are hurtig be!"

Then the Bi-Coloured-Python-Rock-Snake scuffled down from the bank and said, "My young friend, if you do not now, immediately and instantly, pull as hard as ever you can, it is my opinion that your acquaintance in the large-pattern leather ulster" (and by this he meant the Crocodile) "will jerk you into yonder limpid stream before you can say Jack Robinson."

This is the way Bi-Coloured-Python-Rock-Snakes always talk.

Then the Elephant's Child sat back on his little haunches, and pulled, and pulled, and pulled, and his nose began to stretch. And the Crocodile floundered into the water, making it all creamy with great sweeps of his tail, and *he* pulled, and pulled, and pulled.

And the Elephant's Child's nose kept on stretching; and the Elephant's Child spread all his little four legs and pulled, and pulled, and pulled, and his nose kept on stretching; and the Crocodile threshed his tail like an oar, and *he* pulled, and pulled, and pulled, and at each pull the Elephant's Child's nose grew longer and longer—and it hurt him hijjus!

Then the Elephant's Child felt his legs slipping, and he said through his nose, which was now nearly five feet long, "This is too butch for be!"

Then the Bi-Coloured-Python-Rock-Snake came down from the bank, and knotted himself in a double clove hitch round the Elephant's Child's hind legs, and said, "Rash and inexperienced traveller, we will now seriously devote ourselves to a little high tension, because if we do not, it is my impression that yonder self-propelling man-of-war with the armour-plated upper deck" (and by this, O Best Beloved, he meant the Crocodile) "will permanently vitiate your future career."

That is the way all Bi-Coloured-Python-Rock-Snakes always talk.

So he pulled, and the Elephant's Child pulled, and the Crocodile pulled; but the Elephant's Child and the Bi-Coloured-Python-Rock-Snake pulled hardest; and at last the Crocodile let go of the Elephant's Child's nose with a plop that you could hear all up and down the Limpopo.

Then the Elephant's Child sat down most hard and sudden; but first he was careful to say "Thank you" to the Bi-Coloured-Python-Rock-Snake; and next he was kind to his poor pulled nose, and wrapped it all up in cool banana leaves, and hung it in the great grey-green, greasy Limpopo to cool.

"What are you doing that for?" said the Bi-Coloured-Python-Rock-Snake.

" 'Scuse me," said the Elephant's Child, "but my nose is badly out of shape, and I am waiting for it to shrink."

"Then you will have to wait a long time," said the Bi-Coloured-Python-Rock-Snake. "Some people do not know what is good for them."

The Elephant's Child sat there for three days waiting for his nose to shrink. But it never grew any shorter, and, besides, it made him squint. For, O Best Beloved, you will see and understand that the Crocodile had pulled it out into a really truly trunk same as all Elephants have today.

At the end of the third day a fly came and stung him on the shoulder, and before he knew what he was doing he lifted up his trunk and hit that fly dead with the end of it.

" 'Vantage number one!" said the Bi-Coloured-Python-Rock-Snake. "You couldn't have done that with a mere-smear nose. Try and eat a little now."

Before he thought what he was doing the Elephant's Child put out his trunk and plucked a large bundle of grass, dusted it clean against his forelegs, and stuffed it into his own mouth.

" 'Vantage number two!" said the Bi-Coloured-Python-Rock-Snake. "You couldn't have done that with a mere-smear nose. Don't you think the sun is very hot here?"

"It is," said the Elephant's Child, and before he thought what he was doing he schlooped up a schloop of mud from the banks of the great grey-green, greasy Limpopo, and slapped it on his head, where it made a cool schloopy-sloshy mud-cap all trickly behind his ears.

" 'Vantage number three!" said the Bi-Coloured-Python-Rock-Snake. "You couldn't have done that with a mere-smear nose. Now how do you feel about being spanked again?"

" 'Scuse me," said the Elephant's Child, "But I should not like it at all."

"How would you like to spank somebody?" said the Bi-Coloured-Python-Rock-Snake.

"I should like it very much indeed," said the Elephant's Child.

"Well," said the Bi-Coloured-Python-Rock-Snake, "you will find that new nose of yours very useful to spank people with."

"Thank you," said the Elephant's Child, "I'll remember that; and now I think I'll go home to all my dear families and try."

So the Elephant's Child went home across Africa frisking and whisking his trunk. When he wanted fruit to eat he pulled fruit down from a tree, instead of waiting for it to fall as he used to do. When he wanted grass he plucked grass up from the ground, instead of going on his knees as he used to do. When the flies bit him he broke off the branch of a tree and used it as a fly-whisk; and he made himself a new, cool, slushy-squshy mud-cap whenever the sun was hot. When he felt lonely walking through Africa he sang to himself down his trunk, and the noise was louder than several brass bands. He went especially out of his way to find a broad Hippopotamus (she was no relation of his), and he spanked her very hard, to make sure that the Bi-Coloured-Python-Rock-Snake had spoken the truth about his new trunk. The rest of the time he picked up the melon rinds that he had dropped on his way to the Limpopo—for he was a Tidy Pachyderm.

One dark evening he came back to all his dear families, and he coiled up his trunk and said, "How do you do?" They were very glad to see him and immediately said, "Come here and be spanked for your 'satiable curtiosity."

"Pooh," said the Elephant's Child. "I don't think you people know anything about spanking; but *I* do, and I'll show you."

Then he uncurled his trunk and knocked two of his dear brothers head over heels.

"O Bananas!" said they, "where did you learn that trick, and what have you done to your nose?"

"I got a new one from the Crocodile on the banks of the great grey-green, greasy Limpopo River," said the Elephant's Child. "I asked him what he had for dinner, and he gave me this to keep."

"It looks very ugly," said his hairy uncle, the Baboon.

"It does," said the Elephant's Child. "But it's very useful," and he picked up his hairy uncle, the Baboon, by one hairy leg, and hove him into a hornet's nest.

Then that bad Elephant's Child spanked all his dear families for a long time, till they were very warm and greatly astonished. He pulled out his tall Ostrich aunt's tail-feather; and he caught his tall uncle, the Giraffe, by the hind leg, and dragged him through a thorn bush; and he shouted at his broad aunt, the Hippopotamus, and blew bubbles into her ear when she was sleeping in the water after meals; but he never let anyone touch Kolokolo Bird.

At last things grew so exciting that his dear families went off one by one in a hurry to the banks of the great grey-green, greasy Limpopo River, all set about with fever-trees, to borrow new noses from the Crocodile. When they came back nobody spanked anybody any more; and ever since that day, O Best Beloved, all the Elephants you will ever see, besides all those that you won't, have trunks precisely like the trunk of the 'satiable Elephant's Child.

There stood a miserable little hut on hens' legs.

VASILISSA THE BEAUTIFUL

Russian folktale
as told by Post Wheeler

In a certain Tsardom, across three times nine kingdoms, beyond high mountain chains, there once lived a merchant. He had been married for twelve years, but in that time there had been born to him only one child, a daughter, who from her cradle was called Vasilissa the Beautiful. When the little girl was eight years old the mother fell ill, and before many days it was plain to be seen that she must die. So she called her little daughter to her, and taking a tiny wooden doll from under the blanket of the bed, put it into her hands and said:

"My little Vasilissa, my dear daughter, listen to what I say, remember well my last words and fail not to carry out my wishes. I am dying, and with my blessing, I leave to thee this little doll. It is very precious, for there is no other like it in the whole world. Carry it always about with thee in thy pocket and never show it to anyone. When evil threatens thee or sorrow befalls thee, go into a corner, take it from thy pocket and give it something to eat and drink. It will eat and drink a little, and then thou mayest tell it thy trouble and ask its advice, and it will tell thee how to act in thy time of need." So saying, she kissed her little daughter on the forehead, blessed her, and shortly after died.

Little Vasilissa grieved greatly for her mother, and her sorrow was so deep that when the dark night came, she lay in her bed and wept and did not sleep. At length she bethought herself of the tiny doll, so she rose and took it from the pocket of her gown and, finding a piece of wheat bread and a cup of kvass, she set them before it and said: "There, my little doll, take it. Eat a little, and drink a little, and listen to my grief. My dear mother is dead and I am lonely for her."

Then the doll's eyes began to shine like fireflies, and suddenly it became alive. It ate a morsel of the bread and took a sip of the kvass, and when it had eaten and drunk, it said: "Don't weep, little Vasilissa. Grief is worst at night. Lie down, shut thine eyes, comfort thyself, and go to sleep. The morning is wiser than the evening." So Vasilissa the Beautiful lay down, comforted herself, and went to sleep, and the next day her grieving was not so deep and her tears were less bitter.

Now after the death of his wife, the merchant sorrowed for many days as was right, but at the end of that time he began to desire to marry again and to look about him for a suitable wife. This was not difficult to find, for he had a fine house, with a stable of swift horses, besides being a good man who gave much to the poor. Of all the women he saw, however, the one who, to his mind, suited him best of all was a widow of about his own age with two daughters of her own, and she, he thought, besides being a good housekeeper, would be a kind foster mother to his little Vasilissa.

So the merchant married the widow and brought her home as his wife, but the little girl soon found that her foster mother was very far from being what her father had thought. She was a cold, cruel woman who had desired the merchant for the sake of his wealth and had no love for his daughter. Vasilissa was the greatest beauty in the whole village, while her own daughters were as spare and homely as two crows, and because of this all three envied and hated her. They gave her all sorts of errands to run and difficult tasks to perform, in order that the toil might make her thin and worn and that her face might grow brown from sun and wind, and they treated her so cruelly as to leave few joys in life for her. But all this the little Vasilissa endured without complaint, and while the stepmother's two daughters grew always thinner and uglier, in spite of the fact that they had no hard tasks to do, never went out in cold or rain, and sat always with their arms folded like ladies of a Court, she herself had cheeks like blood and milk and grew every day more and more beautiful.

Now the reason for this was the tiny doll, without whose help little Vasilissa could never have managed to do all the work that was laid upon her. Each night, when everyone else was sound asleep, she would get up from her bed, take the doll into a closet, and locking the door, give it something to eat and drink, and say: "There, my little doll, take it. Eat a little, drink a little, and listen to my grief. I live in my father's house, but my spiteful stepmother wishes to drive me out of the white world. Tell me! How shall I act, and what shall I do?"

Then the little doll's eyes would begin to shine like glowworms, and it would become alive. It would eat a little food, and sip a little drink, and then it would comfort her and tell her how to act. While Vasilissa slept, it would get ready all her work for the next day, so that she had only to rest in the shade and gather flowers, for the doll would have the kitchen garden weeded, and the beds of cabbage watered, and plenty of fresh water brought from the well, and the stoves heated exactly right. And, besides this, the little doll told her how to make, from a certain herb, an ointment which prevented her from ever being sunburned. So all the joy in life that came to Vasilissa came to her through the tiny doll that she always carried in her pocket.

Years passed, till Vasilissa grew up and became of an age when it is good to marry. All the young men in the village, high and low, rich and poor, asked for her hand, while not one of them stopped even to look at the stepmother's two daughters, so ill-favored were they. This angered their mother still more against Vasilissa. She answered every gallant who came with the same words: "Never shall the younger be wed before the older ones!" And each time, when she had let a suitor out of the door, she would soothe her anger and hatred by beating her stepdaughter. So while Vasilissa grew each day more lovely and graceful, she was often miserable, and but for the little doll in her pocket, would have longed to leave the white world.

Now there came a time when it became necessary for the merchant to leave his home and to travel to a distant Tsardom. He bade farewell to his wife and her two daughters, kissed Vasilissa and gave her his blessing, and departed, bidding them say a prayer each day for his safe return. Scarce was he out of sight of the village, however, when his wife sold his house, packed all his goods, and moved with them to another dwelling far from the town, in a gloomy neighborhood on the edge of a wild forest. Here every day, while her two daughters were working indoors, the merchant's wife would send Vasilissa on one errand or other into the forest, either to find a branch of a certain rare bush or to bring her flowers or berries.

Now deep in this forest, as the stepmother well knew, there was a green lawn, and on the lawn stood a miserable little hut on hens' legs, where lived a certain Baba-Yaga, an old witch grandmother. She lived alone and none dared go near the hut, for she ate people as one eats chickens. The merchant's wife sent Vasilissa into the forest each day, hoping she might meet the old witch and be devoured. But always the girl came home safe and sound, because the little doll showed her where the bush, the flowers, and the berries grew, and did not let her go near the hut that stood on hens' legs. And each time the stepmother hated her more and more because she came to no harm.

One autumn evening the merchant's wife called the three girls to her and gave them each a task. One of her daughters she bade make a piece of lace, the other to knit a pair of hose, and to Vasilissa she gave a basket of flax to be spun. She bade each finish a certain amount. Then she put out all the fires in the house, leaving only a single candle lighted in the room where the three girls worked, and she herself went to sleep.

They worked an hour, they worked two hours, they worked three hours, when one of the elder daughters took up the tongs to straighten the wick of the candle. She pretended to do this awkwardly (as her mother had bidden her) and put the candle out, as if by accident.

"What are we to do now?" asked her sister. "The fires are all out, there is no other light in all the house, and our tasks are not done."

"We must go and fetch fire," said the first. "The only house near is a hut in the forest, where a Baba-Yaga lives. One of us must go and borrow fire from her."

"I have enough light from my steel pins," said the one who was making the lace, "and *I* will not go."

"And I have plenty of light from my silver needles," said the other, who was knitting the hose, "and I will not go."

"Thou, Vasilissa," they both said, "shalt go and fetch the fire, for thou hast neither steel pins nor silver needles and cannot see to spin thy flax!" They both rose up, pushed Vasilissa out of the house and locked the door, crying: "Thou shalt not come in till thou hast fetched the fire."

Vasilissa sat down on the doorstep, took the tiny doll from one pocket and from another the supper she had ready for it, put the food before it, and said: "There, my little doll, take it. Eat a little and listen to my sorrow. I must go to the hut of the old Baba-Yaga in the dark forest to borrow some fire, and I fear she will eat me. Tell me! What shall I do?"

Then the doll's eyes began to shine like two stars and it became alive. It ate a little and said: "Do not fear, little Vasilissa. Go where thou hast been sent. While I am with thee no harm shall come to thee from the old witch." So Vasilissa put the doll back into her pocket, crossed herself, and started out into the dark, wild forest.

Whether she walked a short way or a long way the telling is easy, but the journey was hard. The wood was very dark, and she could not help trembling from fear. Suddenly she heard the sound of a horse's hoofs, and a man on horseback galloped past her. He was dressed all in white, the horse under him was milk-white and the harness was white, and just as he passed her it became twilight.

She went a little farther, and again she heard the sound of horse's hoofs, and there came another man on horseback galloping past her. He was dressed all in red, and the horse under him was blood-red and its harness was red, and just as he passed her the sun rose.

That whole day Vasilissa walked, for she had lost her way. She could find no path at all in the dark wood, and she had no food to set before the little doll to make it alive.

But at evening she came all at once to the green lawn where the wretched little hut stood on its hens' legs. The wall around the hut was made of human bones, and on its top were skulls. There was a gate in the wall, whose hinges were the bones of human feet and whose locks were jawbones set with sharp teeth. The sight filled Vasilissa with horror, and she stopped as still as a post buried in the ground.

As she stood there, a third man on horseback came galloping up. His face was black, he was dressed all in black, and the horse he rode was coal-black. He galloped up to the gate of the hut and disappeared there as if he had sunk through the ground, and at that moment the night came and the forest grew dark.

But it was not dark on the green lawn, for instantly the eyes of all the skulls on the wall were lighted up and shone till the place was as bright as day. When she saw this Vasilissa trembled so with fear that she could not run away.

Then suddenly the wood became full of a terrible noise. The trees began to groan, the branches to creak and the dry leaves to rustle, and the Baba-Yaga came flying from the forest. She was riding in a great iron mortar and driving it with the pestle, and as she came she swept away her trail behind her with a kitchen broom.

She rode up to the gate, and stopping, said:

Little House, little House,
Stand the way thy mother placed thee,
Turn thy back to the forest and thy face to me!

And the little hut turned facing her and stood still. Then smelling all around her, she cried: "Foo! Foo! I smell a smell that is Russian. Who is here?"

Vasilissa, in great fright, came nearer to the old woman and, bowing very low, said: "It is only Vasilissa, grandmother. My stepmother's daughters sent me to thee to borrow some fire."

"Well," said the old witch, "I know them. But if I give thee the fire thou shalt stay with me some time and do some work to pay for it. If not, thou shalt be eaten for my supper." Then she turned to the gate and shouted: "Ho! Ye, my solid locks, unlock! Thou, my stout gate, open!" Instantly the locks unlocked, the gate opened of itself, and the Baba-Yaga rode in whistling. Vasilissa entered behind her, and immediately the gate shut again and the locks snapped tight.

When they had entered the hut the old witch threw herself down on the stove, stretched out her bony legs, and said: "Come, fetch and put on the table at once everything that is in the oven. I am hungry." So Vasilissa ran and lighted a splinter of wood from one of the skulls on the wall, and took the food from the oven and set it before her. There was enough cooked meat for three strong men. She brought also from the cellar kvass, honey, and red wine, and the Baba-Yaga ate and drank the whole, leaving the girl only a little cabbage soup, a crust of bread, and a morsel of suckling pig.

When her hunger was satisfied, the old witch, growing drowsy, lay down on the stove and said: "Listen to me well, and do what I bid thee. Tomorrow when I drive away, do thou clean the yard, sweep the floors, and cook my supper. Then take a quarter of a measure of wheat from my storehouse and pick out of it all the black grains and the wild peas. Mind thou dost all that I have bade. If not, thou shalt be eaten for my supper."

Presently the Baba-Yaga turned toward the wall and began to snore, and Vasilissa knew that she was fast asleep. Then she went into the corner, took the tiny doll from her pocket, put before it a bit of bread and a little cabbage soup that she had saved, burst into tears and said: "There, my little doll, take it. Eat a little, drink a little, and listen to my grief. Here I am in the house of the old witch, and the gate in the wall is locked, and I am afraid. She has given me a difficult task, and if I do not do all she has bade, she will eat me tomorrow. Tell me: What shall I do?"

Then the eyes of the little doll began to shine like two candles. It ate a little of the bread and drank a little of the soup and said: "Do not be afraid, Vasilissa the Beautiful. Be comforted. Say thy prayers, and go to sleep. The morning is wiser than the evening." So Vasilissa trusted the little doll and was comforted. She said her prayers, lay down on the floor, and went fast asleep.

When she woke next morning, very early, it was still dark. She rose and looked out of the window, and she saw that the eyes of the skulls on the wall were growing dim. As she looked, the man dressed all in white, riding the milk-white horse, galloped swiftly around the corner of the hut, leaped the wall and disappeared, and as he went, it became quite light and the eyes of the skulls flickered and went out. The old witch was in the yard. Now she began to whistle and the great iron mortar and pestle and the kitchen broom flew out of the hut to her. As she got into the mortar the man dressed all in red, mounted on the blood-red horse, galloped like the wind around the corner of the hut, leaped the wall and was gone, and at that moment the sun rose. Then the Baba-Yaga shouted: "Ho! Ye, my solid locks, unlock! Thou, my stout gate, open!" And the locks unlocked and the gate opened, and she rode away in the mortar, driving with the pestle and sweeping away her path behind her with the broom.

When Vasilissa found herself left alone, she examined the hut, wondering to find it filled with such an abundance of everything. Then she stood still, remembering all the work that she had been bidden to do and wondering what to begin first. But as she looked she rubbed her eyes, for the yard was already neatly cleaned and the floors were nicely swept, and the little doll was sitting in the storehouse picking the last black grains and wild peas out of the quarter-measure of wheat.

Vasilissa ran and took the little doll in her arms. "My dearest little doll!" she cried. "Thou has saved me from my trouble! Now I have only to cook the Baba-Yaga's supper, since all the rest of the tasks are done!"

"Cook it, with God's help," said the doll, "and then rest, and may the cooking of it make thee healthy!" And so saying it crept into her pocket and became again only a little wooden doll.

So Vasilissa rested all day and was refreshed, and when it grew toward evening she laid the table for the old witch's supper and sat looking out of the window, waiting for her coming. After a while she heard the sound of a horse's hoofs, and the man in black, on a coal-black horse, galloped up to the wall gate and disappeared like a great dark shadow, and instantly it became quite dark and the eyes of all the skulls began to glitter and shine.

Then all at once the trees of the forest began to creak and groan, and the leaves and the bushes to moan and sigh, and the Baba-Yaga came riding out of the dark wood in the huge iron mortar, driving with the pestle and sweeping out the trail behind her with the kitchen broom. Vasilissa let her in, and the witch, smelling all around her, asked: "Well, hast thou done perfectly all the tasks I gave thee to do, or am I to eat thee for my supper?"

"Be so good as to look for thyself, grandmother," answered Vasilissa.

The Baba-Yaga went all about the place tapping with her iron pestle and carefully examining everything. But so well had the little doll done its work that, try as hard as she might, she could not find anything to complain of. There was not a weed left in the yard, nor a speck of dust on the floors, nor a single black grain or wild pea in the wheat.

The old witch was greatly angered, but was obliged to pretend to be pleased. "Well," she said, "thou hast done all well." Then, clapping her hands, she shouted: "Ho! my faithful servants! Friends of my heart! Haste and grind my wheat!" Immediately three pairs of hands appeared, seized the measure of wheat, and carried it away.

The Baba-Yaga sat down to supper, and Vasilissa put before her all the food from the oven, with kvass, honey, and red wine. The old witch ate it, bones and all, almost to the last morsel, enough for four strong men. And then, growing drowsy, she stretched her bony legs on the stove and said: "Tomorrow do as thou hast done today, and besides these tasks take from my storehouse a half-measure of poppy seeds and clean them one by one. Someone has mixed earth with them to do me a mischief and to anger me, and I will have them made perfectly clean." So saying she turned to the wall and soon began to snore.

When she was fast asleep Vasilissa went into the corner, took the little doll from her pocket, set before it a part of the food that was left, and asked its advice. And the doll, when it had become alive and eaten a little food and sipped a little drink, said: "Don't worry, beautiful Vasilissa! Be comforted. Do as thou didst last night: say thy prayers and go to sleep." So Vasilissa was comforted. She said her prayers and went to sleep and did not wake till next morning, when she heard the old witch in the yard whistling. She ran to the window just in time to see her take her place in the big iron mortar, and as she did so the man dressed all in red, riding on the blood-red horse, leaped over the wall and was gone, just as the sun rose over the wild forest.

As it had happened on the first morning, so it happened now. When Vasilissa looked she found that the little doll had finished all the tasks except the cooking of the supper. The yard was swept and in order, the floors were as clean as new wood, and there was not a grain of earth left in the half-measure of poppy seeds. She rested and refreshed herself till the afternoon, when she cooked the supper, and when evening came she laid the table and sat down to wait for the old witch's coming.

Soon the man in black, on the coal-black horse, galloped up to the gate, and the dark fell and the eyes of the skulls began to shine like day. Then the ground began to quake, and the trees of the forest began to creak and the dry leaves to rustle, and the Baba-Yaga came riding in her iron mortar, driving with her pestle and sweeping away her path with her broom.

When she came in she smelled around her and went all about the hut, tapping with the pestle. But pry and examine as she might, again she could see no reason to find fault and was angrier than ever. She clapped her hands and shouted: "Ho! my trusty servants! Friends of my soul! Haste and press the oil out of my poppy seeds!" And instantly the three pairs of hands appeared, seized the measure of poppy seeds, and carried it away.

Presently the old witch sat down to supper and Vasilissa brought all she had cooked, enough for five grown men, and set it before her, and brought beer and honey, and then she herself stood silently waiting. The Baba-Yaga ate and drank it all, every morsel, leaving not so much as a crumb of bread. Then she said snappishly: "Well, why dost thou say nothing, but stand there as if thou was dumb?"

"I spoke not," Vasilissa answered, "because I dared not. But if thou wilt allow me, grandmother, I wish to ask thee some questions."

"Well," said the old witch, "only remember that every question does not lead to good. If thou knowest overmuch, thou wilt grow old too soon. What wilt thou ask?"

"I would ask thee," said Vasilissa, "of the men on horseback. When I came to thy hut, a rider passed me. He was dressed all in white and he rode a milk-white horse. Who was he?"

"That was my white, bright day," answered the Baba-Yaga angrily. "He is a servant of mine, but he cannot hurt thee. Ask me more."

"Afterwards," said Vasilissa, "a second rider overtook

me. He was dressed in red and the horse he rode was blood-red. Who was he?"

"That was my servant, the round, red sun," answered the Baba-Yaga, "and he, too, cannot injure thee." And she ground her teeth. "Ask me more."

"A third rider," said Vasilissa, "came galloping up to the gate. He was black, his clothes were black, and the horse was coal-black. Who was he?"

"That was my servant, the black, dark night," answered the old witch furiously. "But he also cannot harm thee. Ask me more."

But Vasilissa, remembering what the Baba-Yaga had said, that not every question led to good, was silent.

"Ask me more!" cried the old witch. "Why dost thou not ask me more? Ask me of the three pairs of hands that serve me!"

But Vasilissa saw how she snarled at her and she answered: "The three questions are enough for me. As thou hast said, grandmother, I would not, through knowing overmuch, become too soon old."

"It is well for thee," said the Baba-Yaga, "that thou didst not ask of them, but only of what thou didst see outside of this hut. Hadst thou asked of them, my servants the three pairs of hands would have seized thee also, as they did the wheat and poppy seeds, to be my food. Now I would ask a question in my turn: How is it that thou hast been able, in a little time, to do perfectly all the tasks I gave thee? Tell me!"

71

Vasilissa was so frightened to see how the old witch ground her teeth that she almost told her of the little doll. But she bethought herself just in time, and answered: "The blessing of my dead mother helps me."

Then the Baba-Yaga sprang up in a fury. "Get thee out of my house this moment!" she shrieked. "I want no one who bears a blessing to cross my threshold! Get thee gone!"

Vasilissa ran to the yard, and behind her she heard the old witch shouting to the locks and the gate. The locks opened, the gate swung wide, and she ran out onto the lawn. The Baba-Yaga seized from the wall one of the skulls with burning eyes and flung it after her. "There," she howled, "is the fire for thy stepmother's daughters. Take it. That is what they sent thee here for, and may they have joy of it!"

Vasilissa put the skull on the end of a stick and darted away through the forest, running as fast as she could and finding her path by the skull's glowing eyes, which went out only when morning came.

Whether she ran a long way or a short way, and whether the road was smooth or rough, towards evening of the next day, when the eyes in the skull were beginning to glimmer, she came out of the dark, wild forest to her stepmother's house.

When she came near the gate, she thought, "Surely, by this time they will have found some fire," and threw the skull into the hedge. But it spoke to her, and said:

"Do not throw me away, beautiful Vasilissa. Bring me to thy stepmother." So, looking at the house and seeing no spark of light in any of the windows, she took up the skull again and carried it with her.

Now since Vasilissa had gone, the stepmother and her two daughters had had neither fire nor light in all the house. When they struck flint and steel the tinder would not catch, and the fire they brought from the neighbors would go out immediately as soon as they carried it over the threshold, so that they had been unable to light or warm themselves or to cook food to eat. Therefore now, for the first time in her life, Vasilissa found herself welcomed. They opened the door to her, and the merchant's wife was greatly rejoiced to find that the light in the skull did not go out as soon as it was brought in. "Maybe the witch's fire will stay," she said, and took the skull into the best room, set it on a candlestick, and called her two daughters to admire it.

But the eyes of the skull suddenly began to glimmer and to glow like red coals, and wherever the three turned or ran the eyes followed them, growing larger and brighter till they flamed like two furnaces, and hotter and hotter till the merchant's wife and her two wicked daughters took fire and were burned to ashes. Only Vasilissa the Beautiful was not touched.

In the morning Vasilissa dug a deep hole in the ground and buried the skull. Then she locked the house and set out to the village, where she went to live with an old woman who was poor and childless. And so she remained for many days, waiting for her father's return from the far-distant Tsardom.

But, sitting lonely, time soon began to hang heavy on her hands. One day she said to the old woman: "It is dull for me, grandmother, to sit idly hour by hour. My hands want work to do. Go, therefore, and buy me some flax, the best and finest to be found anywhere, and at least I can spin."

The old woman hastened and bought some flax of the best sort, and Vasilissa sat down to work. So well did she spin that the thread came out as even and fine as a hair, and presently there was enough to begin to weave. But so fine was the thread that no frame could be found to weave it upon, nor would any weaver undertake to make one.

Then Vasilissa went into her closet, took the little doll from her pocket, set food and drink before it, and asked its help. And after it had eaten a little and drunk a little, the doll became alive and said: "Bring me an old frame and an old basket and some hairs from a horse's mane, and I will arrange everything for thee." Vasilissa hastened to fetch all the doll had asked for, and when evening came she said her prayers and went to sleep. In the morning she found ready a frame, perfectly made, to weave her fine thread upon.

74

She wove one month, she wove two months—all the winter Vasilissa sat weaving, weaving her fine thread, till the whole piece of linen was done, of a texture so fine that it could be passed, like thread, through the eye of a needle. When the spring came she bleached it so white that no snow could be compared with it. Then she said to the old woman: "Take thou the linen to the market, grandmother, and sell it, and the money shall suffice to pay for my food and lodging." When the old woman examined the linen, however, she said: "Never will I sell such cloth in the marketplace. No one should wear it except it be the Tsar himself, and tomorrow I shall carry it to the Palace."

Next day, accordingly, the old woman went to the Tsar's splendid Palace and fell to walking up and down before the windows. The servants came to ask her her errand, but she answered them nothing and kept walking up and down. At length the Tsar opened his window and asked: "What dost thou want, old woman, that thou walkest here?"

"O Tsar's Majesty!" the old woman answered, "I have with me a marvelous piece of linen stuff, so wondrously woven that I will show it to none but thee."

The Tsar bade them bring her before him, and when he saw the linen he was struck with astonishment at its fineness and beauty. "What wilt thou take for it, old woman?" he asked.

"There is no price that can buy it, Little Father Tsar," she answered, "but I have brought it to thee as a gift." The Tsar could not thank the old woman enough. He took the linen and sent her to her house with many rich presents.

Seamstresses were called to make shirts for him out of the cloth, but when it had been cut up it was so fine that no one of them was deft and skillful enough to sew it. The best seamstresses in all the Tsardom were summoned but none dared undertake it. So at last the Tsar sent for the old woman and said: "If thou didst know how to spin such thread and weave such linen, thou must also know how to sew me shirts from it."

And the old woman answered: "O Tsar's Majesty, it was not I who wove the linen. It is the work of my adopted daughter."

"Take it, then," the Tsar said, "and bid her do it for me."

The old woman brought the linen home and told Vasilissa the Tsar's command. "Well I knew that the work would needs be done by my own hands," said Vasilissa and, locking herself in her own room, began to make the shirts. So fast and well did she work that soon a dozen were ready. Then the old woman carried them to the Tsar, while Vasilissa washed her face, dressed her hair, put on her best gown, and sat down at the window to see what would happen. And presently a servant in the livery of the Palace came to the house and entering, said: "The Tsar, our lord, desires himself to see the clever needlewoman who has made his shirts and to reward her with his own hands."

Vasilissa rose and went at once to the Palace, and as soon as the Tsar saw her, he fell in love with her with all his soul. He took her by her white hand and made her sit beside him. "Beautiful maiden," he said, "never will I part from thee and thou shalt be my wife."

So the Tsar and Vasilissa the Beautiful were married, and her father returned from the far-distant Tsardom, and he and the old woman lived always with her in the splendid Palace, in all joy and contentment. And as for the little wooden doll, she carried it about with her in her pocket all her life long.

Everybody had a wonderful time.

CEDRIC

Tove Jansson

*This story takes place in Moominvalley, an imaginary
land inhabited by many unusual creatures, such
as hemulens and fillyjonks. Living there, too, are the
Moominfamily—Moominpappa, Moominmamma,
and Moomintroll—and their companions, Sniff
and Snufkin.*

Now, afterwards, it is hard to understand how that
small beast, Sniff, could ever have been persuaded to
give Cedric away.

Never before had Sniff done such a thing, rather the
reverse. And furthermore Cedric really was quite
wonderful.

Cedric wasn't alive, he was a thing—but what a
thing! At first sight he was just a small plush dog,
rather bald and love-worn, but a closer look showed
that his eyes were nearly topazes and that he had a

79

small genuine moonstone on his collar just beside the clasp.

And furthermore he carried an inimitable expression on his face, an expression that no other dog could ever have. Possibly the jewels were more important to Sniff than the expression, but in any case he loved Cedric.

And as soon as he had given Cedric away he regretted it to desperation. He neither ate nor slept nor talked. He only regretted.

"But dearest Sniffy," Moominmamma said worriedly, "if you really did love Cedric so much, then why didn't you at least give him to someone you like and not to Gaffsie's daughter?"

"Pooh," Sniff mumbled, staring at the floor with his poor reddened eyes, "it was Moomintroll's fault. He told me that if one gives something away that one really likes, then one will get it back ten times over and feel wonderful afterwards. He tricked me to it."

"Oh," Moominmamma said. "Well, well." She didn't find anything better to say. She felt she had to sleep on the matter.

Evening fell, and Moominmamma went to bed. Everybody said good night, and the lights were put out, one after the other. Only Sniff lay awake, staring up at the ceiling, where the shadow of a large branch was moving up and down in the moonlight. Through the open window he could hear Snufkin's mouth organ playing in the warm night down by the river.

When Sniff's thoughts became too black he jumped out of bed and padded to the window. He climbed down the rope ladder and ran through the garden where the peonies gleamed white and all the shadows were coal-black. The moon was high, far away and impersonal.

Snufkin was sitting outside his tent.

He didn't play any complete tunes tonight, only small shreds of music that resembled questions or those small concurring sounds one makes when one doesn't know what to say.

Sniff sat down beside him and looked disconsolately into the river.

"Hullo," Snufkin said. "Good thing you came. I've been sitting here thinking about a story that might interest you."

"I'm not interested in fairy tales tonight," Sniff mumbled, wrinkling himself up.

"It's no fairy tale," Snufkin said. "It's happened. It happened to an aunt of my mother's."

And Snufkin started his story, sucking at his pipe and now and then splashing with his toes in the dark river water.

"Once upon a time there was a lady who loved all her belongings. She had no children to amuse or annoy her, she didn't need to work or cook, she didn't mind what people said about her and she wasn't the scared sort. Also she had lost her taste for play. In other words, she found life a bit boring.

"But she loved her beautiful things and she had collected them all her life, sorted them and polished them and made them more and more beautiful to look at. One really didn't believe one's eyes when one entered her house."

"She was a happy lady," Sniff nodded. "What kinds of things did she have?"

"Well," Snufkin said. "She was as happy as she knew how to be. And now don't interrupt me, please. Then, one night it happened that this aunt of my mother's went down to her dark scullery to eat a cold cutlet, and she swallowed a large bone. She felt funny for several days afterwards, and when she didn't get any better she went to her doctor. He tapped her chest and listened to it and X-rayed her and shook her about, and at last he told her that this cutlet bone had stuck crosswise somewhere inside her. It was impossible to pry it loose. In other words, he feared the worst."

"You don't say," Sniff said, showing a little more interest in the story. "He thought the lady was going to kick the bucket but he didn't dare tell her?"

"That's about it," Snufkin agreed. "But this aunt of my mother's wasn't easily scared, so she made him tell her how much time she had left, and then she went home to think. A few weeks wasn't very much.

"She suddenly remembered that in her youth she had wanted to explore the Amazonas, to learn deep-sea diving, to build a large nice house for lonely children, to see a volcano and to arrange a gigantic party for all her friends. But all that was too late now, of course. Friends she had none at all, because she had only collected beautiful things, and that takes time.

"She grew more and more sad while she wandered around in her rooms. Her wonderful belongings gave her no comfort. On the contrary, they only made her think of the day when she'd go to heaven and leave them all behind her.

"And the thought of starting a new collection up there didn't make her at all happy, whatever the reason."

"Poor lady!" Sniff cried. "Couldn't she take the least little thing along with her?"

"No," Snufkin said. "It's not allowed. But now dry up, please, and listen. One night this aunt of my mother's lay awake looking up at the ceiling and brooding. All around her stood lots of beautiful furniture, and all over it were lots of beautiful knickknacks. Her things were everywhere, on the floor, on the walls, on the ceiling, in her cabinets, in her drawers—and suddenly she felt about to suffocate among all those belongings that gave her no comfort at all. And now an idea came to her. It was such a funny idea that this aunt of my mother's began to laugh where she lay. All at once she was feeling fit, and she rose and dressed and started to think.

"She had hit upon the idea to give away everything she owned. That would give her more breathing space, and it's something you need if you've a large bone stuck in your stomach and want to be able to think of the Amazonas."

"How silly," Sniff said disappointedly.

"It wasn't silly in the least," Snufkin objected. "She had lots of fun while she sat thinking out what things to give away to whom.

"She had many relations and knew still more people, you see, that's quite possible even if you've no friends. Well, she thought of everyone, one after the other, and wondered what he or she would like best. It was like a game.

"And she wasn't stupid. To me she gave the mouth organ: Perhaps you haven't known it's gold and rosewood? Well. She thought it out so wisely that everybody got exactly the thing that suited him and that he had dreamt of.

"This aunt of my mother's also had a turn for surprises. She sent all the things in parcels, and the receivers had no idea of who the sender was (they had never been in her home, because she had always been afraid they'd break things).

"It amused her to imagine their astonishment, their thoughts and guesses, and she was feeling quite superior. A little like those fairies that fulfill wishes in a jiffy as they fly along."

"But I didn't send Cedric in a parcel," Sniff cried with bulging eyes. "And I'm not going to die either!"

Snufkin sighed. "You're the same as ever," he said. "But still, try to listen to a good story, can't you, even if it isn't about yourself. And think of me a bit, too. I've saved this story for you, and sometimes I like telling stories. Well, all right. At the same time something else was happening. This aunt of my mother's suddenly found that she was able to sleep at nights, and in the daytime she dreamed of the Amazonas and read books on deep-sea diving and drew plans for that house for children no one wanted. She had fun, and that made herself nicer than usual and people began to like her company. I must beware, she thought. Before I know a word I'll have a lot of friends and no time to arrange that enormous party I've dreamed about. . . .

"Her rooms were becoming airier and airier. She sent off one parcel after the other, and the fewer possessions she had left, the lighter she felt. Finally, she was walking about in empty rooms, feeling rather like a balloon, a happy balloon ready to fly away. . . . "

"To heaven," Sniff observed drily. "Now, listen . . . "

"Don't interrupt me all the time," Snufkin said. "I can hear you're too small for this story. But I'm

86

going to finish it anyway. Good. By and by all her rooms were empty, and this aunt of my mother's had only her bed left.

"It was a large canopied bed, and when her new friends came to visit her it could hold them all, and the smallest ones sat up in the canopy. Everybody had a wonderful time, and her only worry was about that great party which she didn't seem to find the time to have.

"They used to tell ghost stories and funny stories all the night, and then one evening . . ."

"I know, I know," Sniff said crossly. "You're exactly like Moomintroll. I know how it turned out. Then one evening she gave away her bed too and then she went off to heaven and was *so* happy, and the right thing for me to do is to give away not only Cedric but everything I have and then hand in my spade and bucket on top of it all!"

"You're an ass," Snufkin said. "Or, still worse, you're a spoil-story. What I was about to relate was how this aunt of my mother's laughed so terribly at one of the funny stories, that the bone jumped out of her stomach and she became absolutely well!"

"You don't say," Sniff cried, "the poor lady!"

"How do you mean, the poor lady," Snufkin asked.

"Don't you see! She had given all her things away, hadn't she," Sniff cried. "Quite uselessly! Because she didn't die after all! Did she take all her things back then?"

Snufkin bit hard at his pipe and raised his eyebrows.

"You foolish little beast," he said. "She made the whole thing into a funny story. And then she gave a party. And built the house for lonely children. She was too old for deep-sea diving, but she saw the volcano. And then she went off to the Amazonas. That was the last we heard about her."

"Such things cost money," Sniff said with practical disbelief. "She had given everything away, hadn't she?"

"Had she? Indeed?" Snufkin replied. "If you'd have listened as you should you'd remember that she kept the canopied bed, and this bed, my dear Sniff, was made of gold and simply crammed with diamonds and carneoles."

(As for Cedric, Gaffsie made the topazes into eardrops for her daughter and gave Cedric black button eyes instead. One day Sniff found him lying forgotten in the rain and took him back home. The rain had washed away the moonstone which was never found again. But Sniff went on loving Cedric all the same, even if he now did it only for love's sake. And this does him some honor, I believe. —AUTHOR'S NOTE)

"Not now," Dan said quietly. "Later."

FRESH

Philippa Pearce

The force of water through the river gates scoured to a deep bottom; then the river shallowed again. People said the pool below the gates was very deep. Deep enough to drown in anyway.

At the bottom of the pool lived the freshwater mussels. No one had seen them there—most people would not have been particularly interested in them anyway. But if you were poking about among the stones in the shallows below the pool, you couldn't help finding mussel shells occasionally. Sometimes one by itself; sometimes two still hinged together. Grey-blue or green-grey on the outside; on the inside, a faint sheen of mother-of-pearl.

The Webster boys were fishing with their nets in the shallows for minnows, freshwater shrimps—anything that moved—when they found a freshwater mussel that was not just a pair of empty shells.

Dan Webster found it. He said: "Do you want this shell? It's double." While Laurie Webster was saying, "Let's see," Dan was lifting it and had noticed that the two shells were clamped together and that they had unusual weight. "They're not empty shells," he said. "They've something inside. It's alive."

He stooped again to hold the mussel in the palm of his hand so that the river water washed over it. Water creatures prefer water.

Laurie had splashed over to him. Now he crouched with the river lapping near the tops of his Wellington boots. "A freshwater mussel!" he said. "I've never owned one." He put out fingers to touch it—perhaps to take it—as it lay on the watery palm of Dan's hand. Dan's fingers curled up into a protective wall. "Careful," he said.

Together, as they were now, the Webster boys looked like brothers, but they were cousins. Laurie was the visitor. He lived in London and had an aquarium on his bedroom windowsill, instead of a river almost at his back door as Dan had. Dan was older than Laurie; Laurie admired Dan, and Dan was kind to Laurie. They did things together. Dan helped Laurie to find livestock for his aquarium—shrimps, leeches, flatworms, water snails variously whorled; whatever the turned stone and stooping net might bring them. During a visit by Laurie, they would fish often, but—until the last day—without a jam jar, just for the fun of it. On the last day, they took a jam jar and put their more interesting catches into it for Laurie's journey back to London.

Now they had found a freshwater mussel on the second day of Laurie's visit. Five more days still to go.

"We can't keep it," said Dan. "Even if we got the jam jar, it couldn't live in a jam jar for five days. It would be dead by the time you got it back to the aquarium."

Laurie, who was quite young, looked as if he might cry. "I've never had the chance of a freshwater mussel before."

"Well . . . " said Dan. He made as if to put it down among the stones and mud where he had found it.

"Don't! Don't! It's my freshwater mussel! Don't let it go!"

"And don't shout in my ear!" Dan said crossly. "Who said I was letting it go? I was just trying it out in the river again, to see whether it was safe to leave it there. I don't think the current would carry it away."

He put the mussel down in the shelter of a large, slimy stone. The current, breaking on the stone, flowed past without stirring it. But the mussel began to feel at home again. They could almost see it settling contentedly into the mud. After a while it parted the lips of its shells slightly, and a pastrylike substance crowded out a little way.

"What's it *doing*?" whispered Laurie. But this was not the sort of thing that Dan knew, and Laurie would not find out until he got back to his aquarium books in London.

Now they saw that they had not merely imagined the mussel to be settling in. There was less of it visible out of the mud—much less of it.

"It's burying itself. It's escaping," said Laurie. "Don't let it!"

Dan sighed and took the mussel back into the palm of his hand again. The mussel, disappointed, shut up tight.

"We need to keep it in the river," said Dan, "but somewhere where it can't escape."

They looked around. They weren't sure what they were looking for, and at first they certainly weren't finding it.

Still with the mussel in his hand, Dan turned to the banks. They were overhanging, with river water swirling against them and under them. The roots of trees and bushes made a kind of very irregular lattice fencing through which the water ran continually.

"I wonder . . ." said Dan.

"You couldn't keep it there," Laurie said. "It'd be child's play for a freshwater mussel to escape through the roots."

Dan stared at the roots. "I've a better idea," he said. "I'll stay here with the mussel. You go back to our house—to the larder. You'll find a little white plastic carton with Eileen's slimming cress growing in it." Eileen was Dan's elder sister, whose absorbing interest was her figure. "Empty the cress out onto a plate—I'll square Eileen later. Bring the plastic carton back here."

Laurie never questioned Dan. He set off across the meadows towards the house.

Dan and the freshwater mussel were left alone to wait.

Dan was holding the freshwater mussel as he had done before, stooping down to the river with his hand in the water. It occurred to him to repeat the experiment that Laurie had interrupted. He put the mussel down in the lee of the slimy stone again and watched. Again the current left the mussel undisturbed. Again the mussel began to settle itself into the mud between the stones.

Down—gently down—down . . . The freshwater mussel was now as deep in the mud as when Laurie had called out in fear of losing it; but now Laurie was not there. Dan did not interfere. He simply watched the mussel ease itself down—down . . .

Soon less than a quarter of an inch of mussel shell was showing above the mud. The shell was nearly the same colour as the mud embedding it: Dan could identify it only by keeping his eyes fixed continuously upon its projection. That lessened, until it had almost disappeared.

Entirely disappeared . . .

Still Dan stared. As long as he kept his eyes on the spot where the mussel had disappeared, he could get it again. He had only to dig his fingers into the mud at that exact spot to find it. If he let his eyes stray, the mussel was lost forever; there were so many slimy stones like that one, and mud was everywhere. He must keep his eyes fixed on the spot.

"Dan—Dan—Dan!" Laurie's voice came over the meadows. "I've got it!"

He nearly shifted his stare from the spot by the nondescript stone. It would have been so natural to lift his head in response to the calling voice. He was tempted to do it. But he had to remember that this was Laurie's mussel, and it must not be lost; he did remember. He kept his gaze fixed and dug quickly with his fingers and got the mussel again.

There he was standing with the mussel in the palm of his hand, and water and mud dripping from it, when Laurie came in sight. "Is it all right?" he shouted.

"Yes," said Dan.

Laurie climbed down the riverbank into the water with the plastic carton in his hand. Dan looked at it and nodded. "It has holes in the bottom, and we can make some more along the sides with a penknife." He did so, while Laurie held the mussel.

"Now," Dan said, "put the mussel in the carton with some mud and little stones to make it comfortable. That's it. The next thing is to wedge the carton between the roots under the bank at just the right level, so that the water flows through the holes in the carton, without flowing over the whole thing. The mussel will have his flowing river, but he won't be able to escape."

Laurie said, "I wish I could think of things like that."

Dan tried fitting the plastic carton between the roots in several different places, until he found a grip that was just at the right height. Gently he tested the firmness of the wedging, and it held.

"Oh," said Laurie, "it's just perfect, Dan. Thank you. I shall really get it back to the aquarium now. My first freshwater mussel. I shall call it—well, what would *you* call it, Dan?"

"Go on," said Dan. "It's your freshwater mussel. You name it."

"I shall call it Fresh then." Laurie leaned forward to see Fresh, already part buried in his mud, dim in the shadow of the bank, but absolutely a captive. He stood up again and moved back to admire the arrangement from a distance. Then he realized a weakness. "Oh, it'll never do. The plastic's so white. Anyone might notice it and come over to look, and tip Fresh out."

"We'll hide him then," said Dan. He found an old brick among the stones of the shallows and brought it over to the bank roots. He upended the brick in the water, leaning it in a casual pose against the roots, so that it concealed the white plastic carton altogether.

"There," he said.

Laurie sighed. "Really perfect."

"He should be safe there."

"For five days?"

"I tell you what," said Dan, "we could slip down here every day just to have a check on him. To make sure the level of the water through the carton isn't too high or hasn't sunk too low."

Laurie nodded. "Every day."

The daily visit to Fresh was a pleasure that Laurie looked forward to. On the third day it poured with rain, but they put on anoraks as well as boots and made their check as usual. On the fourth day, they reached the riverbank to find a man fishing on the other side of the pool.

The fisherman was minding his own business and only gave them a sidelong glance as they came to a stop on the bank above Fresh's watery dungeon. (They knew its location exactly by now, even from across the meadow.) The man wasn't interested in them—yet. But if they clambered down into the river and began moving old bricks and poking about behind them, he would take notice. He would ask them what they were up to. When they had gone, he would perhaps come over and have a look for himself. He was wearing waders.

"Not now," Dan said quietly. "Later." And they turned away, as though they had come only to look at the view.

They went back after their tea, but the fisherman was still there. In the meantime, Laurie had worked himself into a desperation. "All that rain yesterday has made the river rise. It'll be washing Fresh out of the carton."

"No," said Dan. "You've just got Fresh on the brain. The river's hardly risen at all. If at all. Fresh is all right."

"Why can't that man go home?"

"He'll go home at dusk anyway," said Dan.

"That'll be too late for us. I shall be going to bed by then. You know your mum said I must."

"Yes." Dan looked at him thoughtfully. "Would you like *me* to come? I mean, Mum couldn't stop my being out that bit later than you, because I am that bit older."

"Oh, would you—*would* you?" cried Laurie. "Oh, thanks, Dan."

"Oh, don't thank me," said Dan.

Everything went according to plan, except that Dan, getting down to the river just before dark, found the fisherman still there. But he was in the act of packing up. He did not see Dan. He packed up and walked away, whistling sadly to himself. When the whistling had died away, Dan got down into the river and moved the brick and took out the plastic container. It had been at a safe water level, in spite of the rains, and Fresh was inside, alive and well.

Dan took Fresh out of the carton just to make sure. Then he put him among the stones in the river for the fun of seeing his disappearing act. As he watched, Dan reflected that this was what Fresh would have done if the fisherman *had* spotted the carton and taken him out of it for a good look, and then by mistake dropped him into the water. The fisherman would have lost sight of him, and Fresh would have buried himself. He would have been gone for good—for good, back into the river.

The only signs would have been the brick moved, the plastic container out of place. And Fresh gone. That was all that Dan could have reported to Laurie.

But it had not happened, after all.

Dan picked up Fresh and put him back in the carton and put the carton back, and then the brick, and then walked home. He told Laurie, sitting in his pyjamas in front of the TV with his supper, that everything had been all right. He did not say more.

On the fifth day, the day before Laurie's return to London, they went together to the riverbank. There was no fisherman. The brick was exactly in place and behind it the plastic carton, with the water flowing through correctly. There was Fresh, safe, sound, and apparently not even pining at captivity.

"Tomorrow," said Laurie. "Tomorrow morning we'll bring the jam jar, ready for me to take him home on the train."

That night was the last of Laurie's visit. He and Dan shared Dan's bedroom, and tonight they went to bed at the same time and fell asleep together.

Dan's father was the last person to go to bed at the end of the evening. He bolted the doors and turned out the last lights. That usually did not wake Dan, but tonight it did. Suddenly he was wide awake in the complete darkness, hearing the sound of his parents going to bed in their room, hearing the sound of Laurie's breathing in the next bed, the slow, whispering breath of deep sleep.

The movements and murmurs from the other bedroom ceased; Laurie's breathing continued evenly. Dan still lay wide awake.

He had never really noticed before how very dark everything could be. It was more than blackness; it seemed to fill space as water fills a pool. It seemed to fill the inside of his head.

He lay for some time with the darkness everywhere; then he got up very quietly. He put trousers and sweater on over his pyjamas, bunchily. Laurie's breathing never changed. He tiptoed out of the bedroom and downstairs. In the hall, he put on his Wellington boots. He let himself out of the house and then through the front gate. There was no one about, no lights in the houses, except for a night light where a child slept. There was one lamp in the lane, and that sent his shadow leaping horribly ahead of him. Then he turned a corner and the lamplight had gone. He was taking the short cut towards the river.

No moon tonight. No stars. Darkness . . .

He had been born here; he had always lived here; he knew these meadows as well as he knew himself; but the darkness made him afraid. He could not see the familiar way ahead; he had to remember it. He felt his way. He scented it. He smelled the river before he came to it, and he felt the vegetation changing underfoot, growing ranker when he reached the bank.

He lowered himself into the water, from darkness into darkness. He began to feel along the roots of the bank for the upended brick. He found it quickly—he had not been far out in the point at which he had struck the bank.

His hand was on the brick, and he kept it there while he tried to see. In the darkness and through the darkness, he tried to see what was going to happen— what he was going to make happen. What he was going to do.

Now that he was no longer moving, he could hear the sound of other movements in the darkness.

He heard the water flowing. He heard a *drip* of water into water somewhere near him; a long pause; another *drip*. He heard a quick, quiet birdcall that was strange to him; certainly not an owl—he used to hear those as he lay snug in bed in his bedroom at home. And whatever sound he heard now, he heard beneath it the ceaseless, watery, whispering sound of the river, as if the river were alive and breathing in its sleep in the darkness, like Laurie left sleeping in the bedroom at home.

It was within his power to move the brick and take hold of the plastic carton and tip it right over. Fresh would fall into the water with a *plop* so tiny that he might never hear it above the flow of the river. In such darkness, there would be no question of finding Fresh again, ever.

If he meant to do it, he could do it in three seconds. His hand was on the brick.

But did he mean to do it?

He tried to see what was in his mind, but his mind was like a deep pool of darkness. He didn't know what he really meant to do.

Suddenly he took his hand from the brick and stood erect. He put his booted foot on one of the lateral roots that extended behind the brick. He had to feel for it with his toe. Having found it, he pressed it slowly downwards; then quickly took his foot off again. He could feel the root, released from the pressure, following his foot upwards again in a little jerk.

That jerk of the root might have been enough to upset or at least tilt the carton. It might have been enough to tip Fresh out into the river.

On the other hand, of course, it might not have been enough.

Dan flung himself at the bank well to one side of the brick and clambered up and began a blundering run across the meadows. He did not slow up or go more carefully until he reached the lamplight of the lane and the possibility of someone's hearing his footsteps.

He let himself into the house and secured the door behind him. He left his boots in the hall and his clothes on the chair in the bedroom. He crept back into bed. Laurie was still breathing gently and regularly.

Dan slept late the next morning. He woke to bright sunshine flooding the room and Laurie banging on the bedrail. "Fresh! Fresh! Fresh!" he was chanting. Dan looked at him through eyes half-shut. He was trying to remember a dream he had had last night. It had been a dream of darkness—too dark to remember, or to want to remember. But when he went downstairs to breakfast and saw his boots in the hall with mud still drying on them, he knew that he had not dreamed last night.

Immediately after breakfast, they went down to the river. Laurie was carrying his jam jar.

They climbed down into the shallows as usual. Laurie made a little sound of dismay when he saw the brick. "It's lopsided—the current's moved it!"

Dan stood at a distance in the shallows while Laurie scrabbled the brick down into the water with a splash. There behind it was the white plastic carton, but at a considerable tilt, so that water flowed steadily from its lowest corner. "Oh, Fresh—Fresh!" Laurie implored in a whisper. He was peering into the carton.

"Well?" said Dan, from his distance, not moving.

"Oh, no!" Laurie exclaimed, low but in dismay.

"Well?"

Laurie was poking with a finger at the bottom of the carton. Suddenly he laughed. "He's here after all! It's all right! It was just that burying trick of his! Fresh is here!"

Laurie was beaming.

Dan said, "I'm glad."

Laurie transferred Fresh from the carton to the jam jar, together with some mud and stones and a suitable amount of river water. Dan watched him.

Then they both set off across the meadows again, Laurie holding the jam jar carefully, as he would need to do—as he *would* do—during all the long journey to London. He was humming to himself. He stopped to say to Dan, "I say, I did thank you for Fresh, didn't I?"

"Don't thank me," said Dan.

He quietly sat and enjoyed the world around him.

THE ENCHANTED STICKS

Steven J. Myers

Long ago in Japan, near the city of Kyoto, there was an old man who gathered wood in the forest. He picked up fallen limbs and sticks and traded them to the people of a nearby village for rice and tea.

He lived in a small hut at the edge of the forest by the side of a stream. He caught fish with his bare hands and ate them with his rice. After his evening meal he would sit in his doorway, slowly sip his tea, and quietly enjoy the world around him. He listened to the stream flowing by and the breeze in the leaves of the forest. He smelled the scents of the flowers and grass and fresh water. He felt the air soft and delicate on his skin.

One day when he was out gathering wood a band of twenty robbers jumped out from behind the trees. These robbers were both vicious and fearless. They respected no one and stole and killed without mercy.

The robber chief shouted at the old man and flashed his samurai sword.

The old man bowed in greeting, but showed no fear.

"Do you know who we are?" the robber chief asked.

The old man nodded.

"With this sword I could cut you into a thousand pieces to feed the crows. I could do that and it wouldn't bother me at all."

The old man nodded again.

"Oh, you're too stupid to be afraid!"

The old man bowed once more and smiled.

In the thick forest dark there were only a few shafts of light breaking through from the sky. There was the glint and slashing flash of the robber chief's sword in the rare light. Then, shouting "Hai!" he leaped into the air and with one swift slash he cut off the low limb of a tree. Before it hit the ground, he shouted and slashed so quickly that the limb flew apart in a shower of sticks.

The robber chief laughed and snorted. "Old man, *that* should have been you." And then with a wiggling, waltzing swagger-walk he headed toward Kyoto with his men following in poor and ragged imitation.

The old man gathered up the sticks cut by the robber chief. He took the largest one for a walking stick, and then he tied the rest into a bundle separate from the others because they were green and not much good for kindling.

Walking easily through the forest, slipping between the trees, he started home. Months passed and then one day when the old man was about to make a small fire to heat his tea, he dropped the sticks he was carrying. When he bent down he saw that they had fallen into the shape of the characters that spelled out: *Don't burn us!*

He shook his head and smiled. But when he tried to pick up the sticks, they wiggled in his hands and he dropped them again. And again they arranged themselves to say: *Don't burn us!*

This time he scrunched down to examine them closely. The sticks were from the bundle the robber chief had cut.

There was nothing unusual-looking about them. They were just plain sticks. But as soon as the old man tried to pick up one, it wiggled loose and fell back into its place on the ground.

"All right," the old man said, "I won't burn you."

Then the sticks danced about and arranged themselves into a smiling face.

The old man laughed loudly and the sticks danced about. That only made him laugh more and the sticks dance more until the sticks and the old man were rolling around in dancing laughter.

After that the old man and the sticks *talked* every day. He shook the sticks a few times and tossed them into the air. They fell into words or, sometimes, whole sentences.

109

The old man and the sticks played tic-tac-toe. The old man was always the O's and the sticks were always the X's. The sticks were good at the game, and the old man was pleased no matter who won.

And they would fence: mock sword fights between the old man and one of the sticks. The stick would dance about in the air, swinging and thrusting like the sword of an invisible samurai while the old man fought back with his walking stick. These carefree contests always ended in all the other sticks joining in to make the fight a wild clicking and light clattering of wood. And then the old man would fall down and surrender with laughter.

And when the old man hummed a song while he relaxed after his evening meal, the sticks clacked together beating time to the tune. Or on rare nights the sticks would take tufts of grass and strips of rag to dress themselves as dancers, actors, and animals. Then they would act out the legends from the far past. Afterward they danced, a slow formal dance, their makeshift kimonos flowing in soft waves in the moonlight.

And when the old man told a story, the sticks played the characters—the princes, the dragons, the lions, the lost maidens—as little stick figures, while the old man delighted in their dancing grace.

The old man was content with his life except—except that the band of robbers had grown larger and larger until now there were a hundred of them. No one was safe. They even attacked villages—taking food, clothes, anything they wanted. Then they burned the people's homes and escaped into the forest.

The emperor sent an army after them, but the robbers hid among the trees and thick brush. When the army entered the forest, a rain of arrows shot out of the green dark. Then the robbers jumped out with slashing swords and knives. They were so expert with bow and arrow and sword—especially the chief—that they easily scattered the army.

Then a band of eleven samurai—proud and brave and very skilled with sword and bow—went out to hunt down the robbers. But they got lost in the forest and wandered about, so that when they did find the robbers, the robber chief alone easily killed them.

A few months later the robbers boldly arrived at the outskirts of Kyoto itself, where they kidnapped a young maiden just as she was to marry a prince. The robber chief demanded a ransom so large that no one could pay. So he put the young girl in a bamboo cage and hung it from a tree. He gave her a samisen and ordered her to play and sing for him and his men.

She refused.

He told her that was fine with him, but she would only get rice if she sang. "A bird that doesn't sing isn't worth the bird seed," he said.

So she sang, but only sad songs. And all through the forest people heard her sad music and soft song. But they thought that the robber chief had killed her and that it was only her ghost crying in the trees.

Every evening the old man listened to that song. He felt the sadness that thickened the air and dulled the quality of the light. Each note seemed a separate bird that settled on his skin and sank in to become an ache in his bones. Even the enchanted sticks no longer danced as easily or as lightly.

The old man knew something had to be done—but what? His mind was too clouded, too heavy. A clear stream of action couldn't flow from such a muddied source. So he meditated for three days. He just sat quietly by his hut—eating nothing, doing nothing.

Finally his mind was clear. He would ask the sticks.

He went to the stream for a long, cool drink, then into his hut for the enchanted sticks. He shook them and tossed them into the air.

They said: *You only need a small bundle of us. Follow the maiden's song.*

So he bundled the sticks in a strap, threw them over his shoulder, took his walking stick, and stepped out into the dark, night-tuned forest.

The maiden's music was a thread leading him through the night to the robbers' camp. In a few hours he was at the edge of a lake. Far out in the center he could see an island. By the light of four small fires he could see the shapes and shadows of men. He heard curses and rough voices. Then he saw a bamboo cage swaying from a high limb of a tree. The lovely sad song came from there.

The old man sat down at the edge of the water and waited all through the night. At first one fire was put out, then the second, the third, and finally the last one was only a soft orange-yellow glow. The music stopped. The cage swayed silently. Occasionally sounds of snoring came across the water.

The old man waited until morning. Then, in the early mist, he tossed the sticks into the air. They stuck together as if glued to form a ladder. Taking his walking stick, he climbed to the top. Then the enchanted sticks danced apart to become two tall stilts with the old man, his walking stick over his shoulder, calmly at ease upon them.

He walked out into the lake. The water rose slowly until at its deepest point it came up to his ankles. He paused to stir the water with his stick, rippling his strange reflection. Then he strode toward the island.

Two robbers guarded the island. They were half-asleep. They rubbed their eyes. They yawned. Suddenly one of them saw something move in the mist on the lake. He grabbed the other guard and tried to talk—but he was too frightened.

The second robber yelled, "Ghost! Ghost!" and ran away.

The other robbers, awakened by the screams, came running. The robber on guard jumped up and down and pointed. He still couldn't speak.

The old man continued toward them through the mist. The robbers rubbed their eyes. They thought he was walking on the lake. Some shouted. Others ran for their boats to escape. Others dove into the cold water and tried to swim away.

As the old man got closer to the island, the water became shallow. To the robbers, he appeared to grow taller and taller as he came with his eyes shining in the swirling mist.

The robber chief shouted at his men. He called them cowards. Screaming, "Kill the monster!" he rushed toward the old man.

But now the old man jumped down from his stilts. The sticks fell apart to become a bundle of arrows. He made his strap and walking stick into a bow and shot the enchanted arrows at the robbers. He couldn't miss. If a robber ducked, the arrow would whiz by, stop, and make a sharp turn to return to the target. Arrows curved around trees, jumped over rocks, went underground to pop up behind robbers and hit their bottoms.

Now, all the robbers ran away.

Except for the chief. He stood before the old man and flashed his sword.

The old man stepped forward and raised his walking stick to hit the robber chief.

The robber chief cut the stick in two.

The old man raised both pieces to hit the robber.

The robber slashed quicker than sight—and the 2 sticks were 4.

The old man then raised up 4 pieces to hit the robber.

The robber chief slashed and slashed.

Now the old man had 8 sticks.

The robber slashed.

The old man had 16 sticks.

The robber slashed sixteen times, cutting each stick in two.

The old man hit out with 32 sticks.

The robber, sweat pouring now, slashed thirty-two times.

The old man attacked with 64 sticks.

The robber chief cut those in two.

The old man had 128 sticks.

Now the robber chief was shouting and slashing about in a white-faced frenzy.

The old man attacked with 256 sticks.

The faster the robber chief slashed, the worse it got for him. He shouted "Hai! Hai! Hai!" as he cut and cut.

The old man struck with 512 sticks.

The robber chief was crying now. He was on his knees. Tears, dirt, and sweat covered his face. He tried once more, but his brilliant slashing gave the old man 1,024 sticks to attack with.

The robber fell face-down. Exhausted, he sobbed into the ground.

The old man shook his head, bent down to pick up the robber's sword, and threw it into the deep part of the lake. Then he walked over to the tree with the bamboo cage. He picked up several of his enchanted sticks and made a ladder. He climbed up to help the maiden from her cage. He placed her on his shoulders as he helped her down to the ground. Then he turned his sticks into stilts again. He carried the girl across the lake, where he made the sticks into a bundle. Then he put the girl on his shoulders once more and carried her all the way to her home.

When she told her father and family what had happened, everyone offered rich gifts to the old man.

But he said he only wanted the woods, the stream, and his hut.

The old man returned home, undid his bundle, and dropped the enchanted sticks. They scattered about, but said nothing. They formed no words, made no pictures. The old man tried again. Still nothing. Once more. No words.

He went to the stream, bent down, and scooped out two fish. He cleaned them and put them on a long stick. He got the bundle of enchanted sticks and arranged them into a tent-shaped pile. He took out his flint and struck it to light a handful of dry grass. He set the sticks on fire and cooked his fish. The fish were delicious and the fire crackled and the embers glowed for a long time.

Then the old man took a glowing stick and wrote on the evening air. With the glowing point he made designs, orange-yellow characters, warm-red profiles of lions, dragons, and fish.

And the old man laughed—as free and easy as a child.

"Born a fool, live a fool, die a fool!"

Wisdom's Wages and Folly's Pay

Howard Pyle

Once upon a time there was a wise man of wise men, and a great magician to boot, and his name was Doctor Simon Agricola.

Once upon a time there was a simpleton of simpletons, and a great booby to boot, and his name was Babo.

Simon Agricola had read all the books written by man, and could do more magic than any conjurer that ever lived. But, nevertheless, he was none too well off in the world; his clothes were patched, and his shoes gaped, and that is the way with many another wise man of whom I have heard tell.

Babo gathered rushes for a chairmaker, and he also had too few of the good things to make life easy. But it is nothing out of the way for a simpleton to be in that case.

The two of them lived neighbor to neighbor, the one in the next house to the other, and so far as the world could see there was not a pin to choose between them—only that one was called a wise man and the other a simpleton.

One day the weather was cold, and when Babo came home from gathering rushes he found no fire in the house. So off he went to his neighbor the wise man. "Will you give me a live coal to start my fire?" said he.

"Yes, I will do that," said Simon Agricola, "but how will you carry the coal home?"

"Oh!" said Babo, "I will just take it in my hand."

"In your hand?"

"In my hand."

"Can you carry a live coal in your hand?"

"Oh yes!" said Babo, "I can do that easily enough."

"Well, I should like to see you do it," said Simon Agricola.

"Then I will show you," said Babo. He spread a bed of cold, dead ashes upon his palm. "Now," said he, "I will take the ember upon that."

Agricola rolled up his eyes like a duck in a thunderstorm. "Well," said he, "I have lived more than seventy years, and have read all the books in the world; I have practiced magic and necromancy, and know all about algebra and geometry, and yet, wise as I am, I never thought of this little thing."

That is the way with your wise man.

"Pooh!" said Babo, "that is nothing. I know how to do many more tricks than that."

"Do you?" said Simon Agricola. "Then listen: tomorrow I am going out into the world to make my fortune, for little or nothing is to be had in this town. If you will go along with me I will make your fortune also."

"Very well," said Babo, and the bargain was struck. So the next morning bright and early off they started upon their journey, cheek by jowl, the wise man and the simpleton, to make their fortunes in the wide world, and the two of them made a pair. On they jogged and on they jogged, and the way was none too smooth. By-and-by they came to a great field covered all over with round stones.

"Let us each take one of these," said Simon Agricola. "They will be of use by-and-by," and, as he spoke, he picked up a great stone as big as his two fists, and dropped it into the pouch that dangled at his side.

"Not I," said Babo, "I will carry no stone with me. It is as much as my two legs can do to carry my body, let alone lugging a great stone into the bargain."

"Very well," said Agricola, "*born a fool, live a fool, die a fool.*" And on he tramped, with Babo at his heels.

At last they came to a great wide plain, where, far or near, nothing was to be seen but bare sand, without so much as a pebble or a single blade of grass, and there night caught up with them.

"Dear, dear, but I am hungry!" said Babo.

"So am I," said Simon Agricola. "Let's sit down here and eat."

So down they sat, and Simon Agricola opened his pouch and drew forth the stone.

The stone? It was a stone no longer, but a fine loaf of white bread as big as your two fists. You should have seen Babo goggle and stare! "Give me a piece of your bread, master," said he.

"Not I," said Agricola. "You might have had a dozen of the same kind, had you chosen to do as I bade you and to fetch them along with you. *Born a fool, live a fool, die a fool*," said he; and that was all that Babo got for his supper. As for the wise man, he finished his loaf of bread to the last crumb, and then went to sleep with a full stomach and a contented mind.

The next morning off they started again bright and early, and before long they came to just such another field of stones as they left behind them the day before.

"Come, master," said Babo, "let us each take a stone with us. We may need something more to eat before the day is over."

"No," said Simon Agricola, "we will need no stones today."

But Babo had no notion to go hungry the second time, so he hunted around till he found a stone as big as his head. All day he carried it, first under one arm

122

and then under the other. The wise man stepped along briskly enough, but the sweat ran down Babo's face like drops on the window in an April shower. At last they came to a great wide plain, where neither stock nor stone was to be seen, but only a gallows tree, upon which one poor wight hung dancing upon nothing at all, and there night caught them again.

"Aha!" said Babo to himself. "This time I shall have bread and my master none."

But listen to what happened. Up stepped the wise man to the gallows, and gave it a sharp rap with his staff. Then, lo and behold! The gallows was gone, and in its place stood a fine inn, with lights in the windows, and a landlord bowing and smiling in the doorway, and a fire roaring in the kitchen, and the smell of the good things cooking filling the air all around, so that only to sniff did one's heart good.

Poor Babo let fall the stone he had carried all day. A stone it was, and a stone he let it fall.

"*Born a fool, live a fool, die a fool,*" said Agricola. "But come in, Babo, come in; here is room enough for two." So that night Babo had a good supper and a sound sleep, and that is a cure for most of a body's troubles in this world.

The third day of their traveling they came to farms and villages, and there Simon Agricola began to think of showing some of those tricks of magic that were to make his fortune and Babo's into the bargain.

123

At last they came to a blacksmith's shop, and there was the smith hard at work, dinging and donging, and making sweet music with hammer and anvil. In walked Simon Agricola and gave him good-day. He put his fingers into his purse, and brought out all the money he had in the world; it was one golden angel. "Look, friend," said he to the blacksmith; "if you will let me have your forge for one hour, I will give you this money for the use of it."

The blacksmith liked the tune of that song very well. "You may have it," said he; and he took off his leathern apron without another word, and Simon Agricola put it on in his stead.

Presently, who should come riding up to the blacksmith's shop but a rich old nobleman and three servants. The servants were hale, stout fellows, but the nobleman was as withered as a winter leaf. "Can you shoe my horse?" said he to Simon Agricola, for he took him to be the smith because of his leathern apron.

"No," says Simon Agricola; "that is not my trade; I only know how to make old people young."

"Old people young!" said the old nobleman. "Can you make me young again?"

"Yes," said Simon Agricola, "I can, but I must have a thousand golden angels for doing it."

"Very well," said the old nobleman; "make me young, and you shall have them and welcome."

So Simon Agricola gave the word, and Babo blew the bellows until the fire blazed and roared. Then the doctor caught the old nobleman, and laid him upon the forge. He heaped the coals over him, and turned him this way and that, until he grew red-hot, like a piece of iron. Then he drew him forth from the fire and dipped him in the water tank. Phizz! the water hissed, and the steam rose up in a cloud; and when Simon Agricola took the old nobleman out, lo and behold! He was as fresh and blooming and lusty as a lad of twenty.

But you should have seen how all the people stared and goggled!—Babo and the blacksmith and the nobleman's servants. The nobleman strutted up and down for a while, admiring himself, and then he got upon his horse again. "But wait," said Simon Agricola, "you forgot to pay me my thousand golden angels."

"Pooh!" said the nobleman, and off he clattered, with his servants at his heels; and that was all the good that Simon Agricola had of this trick. But ill-luck was not done with him yet, for when the smith saw how matters had turned out, he laid hold of the doctor and would not let him go until he had paid him the golden angel he had promised for the use of the forge. The doctor pulled a sour face, but all the same he had to pay the angel. Then the smith let him go, and off he marched in a huff.

Outside of the forge was the smith's mother—a poor old creature, withered and twisted and bent as a winter twig. Babo had kept his eyes open, and had not traveled with Simon Agricola for nothing. He plucked the smith by the sleeve: "Look'ee, friend," said he, "how would you like me to make your mother, over yonder, young again?"

"I should like nothing better," said the smith.

"Very well," said Babo, "give me the golden angel that the master gave you, and I'll do the job for you."

Well, the smith paid the money, and Babo bade him blow the bellows. When the fire roared up good and hot, he caught up the old mother, and, in spite of her scratching and squalling, he laid her upon the embers. By-and-by, when he thought the right time had come, he took her out and dipped her in the tank of water; but instead of turning young, there she lay, as dumb as a fish and as black as coal.

When the blacksmith saw what Babo had done to his mother, he caught him by the collar, and fell to giving him such a dressing down as never man had before.

"Help!" bawled Babo. "Help! Murder!"

Such a hubbub had not been heard in that town for many a day. Back came Simon Agricola running, and there he saw, and took it all in in one look.

"Stop, friend," said he to the smith, "let the simpleton go; this is not past mending yet."

"Very well," said the smith, "but he must give me back my golden angel, and you must cure my mother, or else I'll have you both up before the judge."

"It shall be done," said Simon Agricola; so Babo paid back the money, and the doctor dipped the woman in the water. When he brought her out she was as well and strong as ever—but just as old as she had been before.

"Now be off for a pair of scamps, both of you," said the blacksmith, "and if you ever come this way again, I'll set all the dogs in the town upon you."

Simon Agricola said nothing until they had come out upon the highway again, and left the town well behind them; then—"*Born a fool, live a fool, die a fool!*" says he.

Babo said nothing, but he rubbed the places where the smith had dusted his coat.

The fourth day of their journey they came to a town, and here Simon Agricola was for trying his tricks of magic again. He and Babo took up their stand in the corner of the marketplace, and began bawling, "Doctor Knowall! Doctor Knowall! who has come from the other end of Nowhere! He can cure any sickness or pain! He can bring you back from the gates of death! Here is Doctor Knowall! Here is Doctor Knowall!"

Now there was a very, very rich man in that town, whose daughter lay sick to death; and when the news of this great doctor was brought to his ears, he was for having him try his hand at curing the girl.

"Very well," said Simon Agricola, "I will do that, but you must pay me two thousand golden angels."

"Two thousand golden angels!" said the rich man. "That is a great deal of money, but you shall have it if only you will cure my daughter."

Simon Agricola drew a little vial from his bosom. From it he poured just six drops of yellow liquor upon the girl's tongue. Then—lo and behold!—up she sat in bed as well and strong as ever, and asked for a boiled chicken and a dumpling, by way of something to eat.

"Bless you! Bless you!" said the rich man.

"Yes, yes, blessings are very good, but I would like to have my two thousand golden angels," said Simon Agricola.

"Two thousand golden angels! I said nothing about two thousand golden angels," said the rich man. "Two thousand fiddlesticks!" said he. "Pooh! pooh! you must have been dreaming! See, here are two hundred silver pennies, and that is enough and more than enough for six drops of medicine."

"I want my two thousand golden angels," said Simon Agricola.

"You will get nothing but two hundred pennies," said the rich man.

"I won't touch one of them," said Simon Agricola, and off he marched in a huff.

But Babo had kept his eyes open. Simon Agricola had laid down the vial upon the table, and while they were saying this and that back and forth, thinking of nothing else, Babo quietly slipped it into his own pocket, without anyone but himself being the wiser.

Down the stairs stumped the doctor with Babo at his heels. There stood the cook waiting for them.

"Look," said he, "my wife is sick in there; won't you cure her, too?"

"Pooh!" said Simon Agricola, and out he went, banging the door behind him.

"Look, friend," said Babo to the cook, "here I have some of the same medicine. Give me the two hundred pennies that the master would not take, and I'll cure her for you as sound as a bottle."

"Very well," said the cook, and he counted out the two hundred pennies, and Babo slipped them into his pocket. He bade the woman open her mouth, and when she had done so he poured all the stuff down her throat at once.

"Ugh!" said she, and therewith rolled up her eyes, and lay as stiff and dumb as a herring in a box.

When the cook saw what Babo had done, he snatched up the rolling pin and made at him to pound his head to a jelly. But Babo did not wait for his coming; he jumped out of the window, and away he scampered with the cook at his heels.

Well, the upshot of the business was that Simon Agricola had to go back to bring life to the woman again, or the cook would thump him and Babo both with the rolling pin. And, what was more, Babo had to pay back the two hundred pennies that the cook had given him for curing his wife.

The wise man made a cross upon the woman's forehead, and up she sat, as well—but no better—as before.

"And now be off," said the cook, "or I will call the servants and give you both a drubbing for a pair of scamps."

Simon Agricola said never a word until they had gotten out of the town. There his anger boiled over, like water into the fire. "Look," said he to Babo: "*Born a fool, live a fool, die a fool.* I want no more of you. Here are two roads; you take one, and I will take the other."

"What!" said Babo. "Am I to travel the rest of the way alone? And then, besides, how about the fortune you promised me?"

"Never mind that," said Simon Agricola, "I have not made my own fortune yet."

"Well, at least pay me something for my wages," said Babo.

"How shall I pay you?" said Simon Agricola. "I have not a single groat in the world."

"What!" said Babo. "Have you nothing to give me?"

"I can give you a piece of advice."

"Well," said Babo, "that is better than nothing, so let me have it."

"Here it is," said Simon Agricola: *"Think well! Think well! Before you do what you are about to do, think well!"*

"Thank you!" said Babo; and then the one went one way, and the other the other.

(You may go with the wise man if you choose, but I shall jog along with the simpleton.)

After Babo had traveled for a while, he knew not whither, night caught him, and he lay down under a hedge to sleep. There he lay, and snored away like a sawmill, for he was wearied with his long journeying.

Now it chanced that the same night two thieves had broken into a miser's house, and had stolen an iron pot full of gold money. Day broke before they reached home, so down they sat to consider the matter; and the place where they seated themselves was on the other side of the hedge where Babo lay. The older thief was for carrying the money home under his coat; the younger was for burying it until night had come again. They squabbled and bickered and argued till the noise they made wakened Babo, and he sat up. The first thing he thought of was the advice that the doctor had given him the evening before.

"Think well!" he bawled out; *"Think well! Before you do what you are about to do, think well!"*

When the two thieves heard Babo's piece of advice, they thought that the judge's officers were after them for sure and certain. Down they dropped the pot of money, and away they scampered as fast as their legs could carry them.

Babo heard them running, and poked his head through the hedge, and there lay the pot of gold. "Look now," said he. "This has come from the advice that was given me; no one ever gave me advice that was worth so much before." So he picked up the pot of gold, and off he marched with it.

He had not gone far before he met two of the king's officers, and you may guess how they opened their eyes when they saw him traveling along the highway with a pot full of gold money.

"Where are you going with that money?" said they.

"I don't know," said Babo.

"How did you get it?" said they.

"I got it for a piece of advice," said Babo.

For a piece of advice! No, no—the king's officers knew butter from lard, and truth from t'other thing. It was just the same in that country as it is in our town—there was nothing in the world so cheap as advice. Whoever heard of anybody giving a pot of gold and silver money for it? Without another word they marched Babo and his pot of money off to the king.

"Come," said the king, "tell me truly; where did you get the pot of money?"

Poor Babo began to whimper. "I got it for a piece of advice," said he.

132

"Really and truly?" said the king.

"Yes," said Babo, "really and truly."

"Humph!" said the king. "I should like to have advice that is worth as much as that. Now, how much will you sell your advice to me for?"

"How much will you give?" said Babo.

"Well," said the king, "let me have it for a day on trial, and at the end of that time I will pay you what it is worth."

"Very well," said Babo, "that is a bargain"; and so he lent the king his piece of advice for one day on trial.

Now the chief councillor and some others had laid a plot against the king's life, and that morning it had been settled that when the barber shaved him he was to cut his throat with a razor. So after the barber had lathered his face he began to whet the razor.

Just at that moment the king remembered Babo's piece of advice. *"Think well!"* said he; *"Think well! Before you do what you are about to do, think well!"*

When the barber heard the words that the king said, he thought that all had been discovered. Down he fell upon his knees, and confessed everything.

That is how Babo's advice saved the king's life—you can guess whether the king thought it was worth much or little. When Babo came the next morning the king gave him ten chests full of money, and that made the simpleton richer than anybody in all that land.

He built himself a fine house, and by-and-by married the daughter of the new councillor that came after the other one's head had been chopped off for conspiring against the king's life. Besides that, he came and went about the king's castle as he pleased, and the king made much of him. Everybody bowed to him, and all were glad to stop and chat awhile with him when they met him in the street.

One morning Babo looked out of the window, and who should he see come traveling along the road but Simon Agricola himself, and he was just as poor and dusty and travel-stained as ever.

"Come in, come in!" said Babo; and you can guess how the wise man stared when he saw the simpleton living in such a fine way. But he opened his eyes wider than ever when he heard that all these good things came from the piece of advice he had given Babo that day they had parted at the crossroads.

"Aye, aye!" said he. "The luck is with you for sure and certain. But if you will pay me a thousand golden angels, I will give you something better than a piece of advice. I will teach you all the magic that is to be learned from the books."

"No," said Babo, "I am satisfied with the advice."

"Very well," said Simon Agricola. *"Born a fool, live a fool, die a fool"*; and off he went in a huff.

(That is all of this tale except the tip end of it, and
that I will give you now.

I have heard tell that one day the king dropped in
the street the piece of advice that he had bought
from Babo, and that before he found it again it had
been trampled into the mud and dirt. I cannot say
for certain that this is the truth, but it must have been
spoiled in some way or other, for I have never heard
of anybody in these days who would give even so
much as a bad penny for it; and yet it is worth just as
much now as it was when Babo sold it to the king.)

"He acts like a stork."

MR. SINGER'S NICKNAMES

James Krüss

In the month of May of the year 1912 a steamboat came from the City of Hamburg to the Island of Helgoland. On its deck stood two gentlemen, talking to each other. One of them was stout, tall, and completely dressed in black. The other one was small and thin, had a pince-nez on his nose, and wore yellow spats over his shoes.

"Have you ever been on Helgoland?" the stout man asked the thin one.

"No," answered the gentleman with the pince-nez. "I am going over for the first time. I am to be the representative for the Society for the Care of Lobsterfishermen's Widows." He bowed and said, "May I introduce myself: Johann Jakob Singer!"

137

"I'm pleased to meet you, Mr. Singer. My name is Rasmussen, Pastor Rasmussen. But the islanders call me Thunder Pastor."

"Why Thunder Pastor?" asked Mr. Singer.

"Because I thunder into the consciences of the Helgolanders every Sunday," said the pastor. "You must know, Mr. Singer, that everyone who lives on Helgoland has an added name, a nickname."

"How dreadful!" exclaimed Mr. Singer. "But," he added, pursing his lips, "I am sure I will not be awarded any nickname. I am an honorable man who works and does his duty."

"Careful, Mr. Singer. Don't say that too loudly!"

"I shall say it as loudly as I please!" was the angry reply of the gentleman with the yellow spats. And pulling himself up with great dignity he added, "I am willing to wager that the Helgolanders will not give me a nickname!"

"I'll take that bet!" shouted Thunder Pastor with his booming voice. "If you do not have a nickname at the end of the first week, I will row around the island three times in a rowboat."

"Agreed," said Mr. Singer, and he put his skinny hand into the strong paw of the pastor. "Whoever loses the bet has to row around the island three times."

The pastor and the insurance representative promised each other to keep the bet secret and to take a walk together across the island in a week's time, the last Thursday in May, to find out whether or not Mr. Singer had been given a nickname.

It was afternoon when the little steamer reached Helgoland. The captain stopped the motor before they reached the island, let the anchor clank into the water, and lowered a rope ladder from the port side of the ship. Very soon a rowboat came over from the island, and all the passengers had to climb down the rope ladder into the boat. Pastor Rasmussen, who was used to this practice, was the first one down the ladder. He was followed by the timid Mr. Singer, who felt his way with shaky feet from rung to rung. The fishermen down in the boat stared in astonishment at the yellow spats; and the man at the tiller said, "He acts like a stork." Pastor Rasmussen smiled to himself.

When the boat made fast at the pier a quarter hour later, Helgolanders stood to the right and the left in two long lines. These two lines of people were called the razzers, since they tended to make remarks back and forth about newcomers that were not very flattering. When the pastor walked past the razzers, they called from both sides, "Welcome home, Pastor!" An old fisherman shouted, "We haven't had any good Sunday storms in a long time." And the plump owner of a rooming house called, "Hallelujah, it's going to Thunder again!"

The pastor threw a quick glance at Mr. Singer, and the poor insurance representative felt a little sick because he remembered that he didn't even know how to row.

Pastor Rasmussen also noticed a few whispered remarks that he didn't quite catch, which undoubtedly referred to the skinny Mr. Singer. For he did hear, to the left, someone whisper, "Our bird collection will get an owl!" And to the right, someone murmured, "Here comes an umbrella with a little man!"

The Thunder Pastor smiled. He was thinking of the bet. But by the same token he realized that the whispering was not very polite to a guest, and he decided to thunder a sermon on manners at the Helgolanders next Sunday.

Pastor Rasmussen delivered Mr. Singer at the Widow Broders' house on Treppen Street, since that was where the insurance representative was to be housed. He said goodbye to him and promised to call for him exactly a week later for the walk across the island. Then he made his way to the Upper Land to the parsonage.

But no sooner had the pastor climbed halfway up the stairs than the Widow Broders came panting after him calling, "Pastor, Pastor! Pastor!"

"What is it, Mrs. Broders?"

"Pastor, the little parrot that you brought me does not eat fish! What am I going to do? I can't buy meat for him every day. It's too expensive!"

"My dear Mrs. Broders," answered the pastor, raising his voice. "First of all, Mr. Singer is no parrot, remember that; and second, with God's help man can get used to anything, even to fish if it is well prepared. Good day!"

"Good day, I'm sorry to've bothered you," murmured the Widow Broders, tripping peaceably down the stairs. She had made up her mind to see that Mr. Singer got used to fish.

And that she did, and in a very simple way. She served him a whale cutlet and called it Wiener Schnitzel. She gave him smoked shark's belly and pretended it was pork belly right out of the smokehouse. The long and short of it was, she fooled him for several days; and on the fourth day, when Mr. Singer praised her cooking, she told him the truth: that he had eaten nothing but fish for three days.

The insurance representative was completely nonplussed at her announcement. He removed his pince-nez, sniffed the pork chop on his plate, and said, "Don't tell me this is swordfish!"

"Oh no, Mr. Singer," the Widow Broders said, laughing. "Today you are getting real pork, because it's Sunday."

During Johann Jakob Singer's first week on the island, he had many other surprises. For example, on the mainland he shook hands with all the people he met on the street that he knew, saying "Good day" and "How are you?" But on Monday morning this habit made him a whole hour late in getting to the office. During the short walk he met no less than fourteen people who were connected in some way with his insurance business. Fourteen times he held out his hand in greeting. Fourteen times he said, "Good day" and "How are you?" Fourteen times he reached out again in parting, and fourteen times he said, "Take care" and "Goodbye." This was time-consuming, and it was also very unusual on the island of Helgoland. The other people just shook hands when they left for the mainland or came back from there. Otherwise they merely said "Hello" or "Hoi" when they met someone.

The discussions he held in his insurance office also surprised Mr. Singer. As a correct man he always referred to his company as The Society for the Care of Lobsterfishermen's Widows. But the Helgolanders always spoke of it as "The Santa Claus Company." It took three or four days for Mr. Singer to find out that when they said this they meant his Lobsterfishermen's Widows' Insurance Company. The reason behind the name is simple. You see, St. Nicholas is the patron saint of all fishermen and seamen. So all companies that help seamen are called Santa Claus companies. And the representatives of such companies are simply called Nicholas. The representative of the Steamship Insurance Company at that time, for example, was called Nicholas One-two-three, because he always carried a walking cane with an iron tip, which he put down hard after every second step. It sounded like clap-clap-clip, or like one-two-three. The representative for Fisherman's Benefit Association was called Nicholas Pepper, because he showed a liking for highly seasoned food. And the representative of the Pilots' Insurance Company was called Pig Nicholas, because he owned the only pig on the whole island.

Johann Jakob Singer gradually learned all these names, but by the end of the week, as far as he knew, he was still without a nickname himself. And he was very proud of this. When Pastor Rasmussen called for him, as agreed, the last Thursday in May, the insurance representative said, "You have lost the wager, Pastor! I have been on Helgoland a whole week, and I still have no nickname."

"Just wait, Mr. Singer!" laughed the Thunder Pastor. "Let's take our walk first. Come along!"

The insurance representative donned his flowered chartreuse vest and decorated his thin ankles with his lemon-yellow spats. And he set out to accompany the pastor across the island. His office hours were over, since it was five o'clock in the afternoon.

As they climbed the steps to the Upper Land, they had to make a detour around Zangi, the old street sweeper, who was in the process of sweeping the one-hundred-eighty-three steps.

"How are things going, Zangi?" asked Pastor Rasmussen.

The old man answered without raising his head, "Downhill, Pastor!" As he spoke, his work took him down three more steps.

The Thunder Pastor called after him, "Tell me, Zangi, how old are you?"

"Seventy-five, Pastor!"

"Then it's about time for you to retire. Do you have any insurance?"

The old street sweeper hardly stopped sweeping as he answered. "Nope, Pastor, I'm not insured. I'll keep going until the end. Insurance companies just speculate and hope that you'll die early. I know those fellows! Nicholas One-two-three is as shrewd as the devil; Nicholas Pepper is a dunderhead; the Pig Nicholas doesn't like me; and the new Nicholas Lemonfoot isn't going to be much better either."

"Just a minute!" cried Mr. Singer. But by that time Zangi was already twelve steps down and couldn't hear him anymore. He was almost completely deaf.

Johann Jakob Singer stared at his yellow spats and asked, "Why did that fellow call me Lemonfoot? Yellow spats are the latest fashion in Hamburg."

"But not on Helgoland," answered the pastor, grinning. Then he took Mr. Singer's arm and said, "Come along. We'll visit Druggist Melleen."

Both gentlemen had now arrived at the top of the stairs, and they stepped into the old pharmacy which stood just above the stairs at the edge of the rock. They were invited to sit down.

"I have heard a lot about you," said the pharmacist to Mr. Singer. "They call you the Dupe, right?"

"How is that again?" asked the insurance representative, shocked. "Dupe?"

"Oh, don't let it bother you," said Druggist Melleen. "Here no one is called by his right name. I am Ammonia-Peter. And you are called *Dupe*."

"Yes, but why, Mr. Druggist?"

"Well, Mr. Singer, it's like this: the Widow Broders has told everyone that you didn't like fish. But in her house, says the Widow Broders, you learned to eat fish. It took a bit of faking, she says. That's why people call you *Dupe*."

Pastor Rasmussen laughed so heartily he almost choked. But Mr. Singer only said, "How embarrassing!"

As both men sauntered on across the island, the Thunder Pastor said, "Well, you have two nicknames at least. I wonder if there is a third one."

"Two is enough!" said Johann Jakob Singer indignantly. He would have liked nothing better than to turn around. But the pastor dragged him on across the Upper Land, and even treated him to a grog in the tavern, "Joy of the North Sea."

The host himself, Genever-Harry, brought two glasses of grog and sat down with the two gentlemen.

"How do you like our island, Governor?" he asked Mr. Singer.

"I am not the Governor!" said Mr. Singer with dignity.

Genever-Harry laughed. "Of course, I know that you are an insurance agent. But I hear that you shake hands ten times a day with everybody. Only the Governor does that here; he comes to the island and shakes hands once a year. That's why people call you *Governor*. Quite a nice name."

Fortunately, Pastor Rasmussen did not choke this time. But he laughed just as hard. Mr. Singer only said, "Not bad!" because he liked the nickname, *Governor*. He almost enjoyed continuing his walk across the island with the pastor.

It was getting dark when both men approached the lighthouse, which rotated its three lightbeams tirelessly to warn the ships at sea.

At the foot of the lighthouse, they met Antje Howdjado. She was the wife of an Englishman who sold cloth on the island. She never asked, *Wie geht's?* in German. Instead she used the English, *How do you do?* That is why she was called Antje Howdjado.

In the settling darkness, Antje recognized the pastor only by his voice. She did not recognize Mr. Singer at all. So she asked, "With whom are you walking tonight, Pastor?"

"With Mr. Singer, the insurance agent, Antje!"

"Ah, with the Rubber-Nicholas! How do you do?"

"I beg your pardon?" cried Mr. Singer, beside himself. "Rubber-Nicholas?"

"Oh, please don't be offended by the name," said Antje Howdjado. "I meant no harm. I heard it from somebody else."

"But where did they get Rubber-Nicholas?" asked Pastor Rasmussen.

"That's easy, Pastor. It comes from his signature."

"From what?" asked Johann Jakob Singer.

"Well," said Antje Howdjado, "it says below your name on each one of your letters: 'Society for the Care of Lobsterfishermen's Widows, Agent.' That name stretches as long as a rubberband."

"But why do you say *Nicholas*?" asked Mr. Singer, embarrassed.

"Because all insurance agents are called Nicholas here."

"Aha," murmured the agent meekly. "That's why the street sweeper called me Nicholas Lemonfoot."

Pastor Rasmussen burst out in a real horse-laugh and ended with a loud snort. "Serves you right, Singer, that they call you Rubber-Nicholas! How could anyone invent such a monstrous name! How does it go, Antje?"

" 'Society for the Care of Lobsterfishermen's Widows, Agent,' Pastor!"

"Hilarious!" cried the pastor.

Mr. Singer could only whisper, "Dreadful!"

147

Going home, Mr. Singer had to agree that he had completely lost the bet. He had gone down in shame. Instead of just one nickname, he had four of them. It bothered him so much that the pastor really felt sorry for him.

"You know what?" said Pastor Rasmussen. "I can make sure that you are only called *Governor* from now on. That name seems to please you most."

The agent nodded.

"All right. And when do you plan to row three times around the island, Mr. Singer?"

"Maybe on Saturday," mumbled the poor man.

"Very well, Mr. Singer! Saturday morning at nine o'clock a rowboat will be ready for you at the landing dock. I hope you don't mind if I go along for the ride."

The agent shook his head. Totally defeated, he said "Good night," and disappeared quickly into Widow Broders' house.

The next Saturday the islanders were astonished to see the Thunder Pastor and the new insurance agent climb into a rowboat and to see the spindly Mr. Singer strain at the oars and row awkwardly southward. Their astonishment grew as they saw from the edge of the cliff that the little rowboat was going around the entire island.

But everyone went completely wild when the rowboat, after three hours of circumnavigation, did not dock but went south for a second time, heading again around the rock. Now people came streaming out of their houses, and everywhere along the edge of the cliff, the curious gathered to watch the tiny boat down in the water.

The clever pastor had chosen a rowboat for the circular tour that belonged to the government and bore the name, "Governor." This was cunning. Because as soon as Genever-Harry saw the boat from his tavern, "Joy of the North Sea," he shouted, "Hey, folks, look at that. The Governor is rowing the 'Governor' around the island."

This quip flew from mouth to mouth, and in less time than it takes to tell, Johann Jakob Singer had the nickname he liked best. Rowing past the dock for the second time without stopping, everyone was already shouting: "Hello, Governor, are you trying to set an endurance record for rowing?"

Johann Jakob Singer nodded and was happy. This for two reasons: first, because they had called him *Governor;* and second, because he had now learned to row. He moved the oars almost as gracefully as a bird moves his wings, lightly and in rhythm, without even thinking.

Late in the afternoon, when he had finally rowed around the island three times and had fastened the boat at the little dock, he was immediately made an honorary member of the Rowing Club, "Heave-ho," and, together with the pastor, was taken to the tavern, "Joy of the North Sea."

For the next few days, the Widow Broders was almost overcome by the change in Mr. Singer. He no longer wore his yellow spats; he called his insurance business Nicholas Society; he often ate fish and liked it—even snails; he no longer shook hands with people ten times a day, but called "Hello" or "Hoi" when he met someone; and one day he even went to his office in a blue fisherman's sweater.

"You know, Governor," said the widow one Sunday during dinner. "It's getting hard to tell that you're not a Helgolander."

"That's right!" said Mr. Singer. And he pushed aside the pork chop the widow had put down and reached for the freshly smoked sharkbelly.

"Who stole the tarts?"

ALICE'S ADVENTURES IN WONDERLAND

Lewis Carroll

CHAPTER I

DOWN THE RABBIT-HOLE

Alice was beginning to get very tired of sitting by her sister on the bank, and of having nothing to do: once or twice she had peeped into the book her sister was reading, but it had no pictures or conversations in it, "And what is the use of a book," thought Alice, "without pictures or conversations?"

So she was considering in her own mind (as well as she could, for the hot day made her feel very sleepy and stupid) whether the pleasure of making a daisy-chain would be worth the trouble of getting up and picking the daisies, when suddenly a white rabbit with pink eyes ran close by her.

There was nothing so *very* remarkable in that; nor did Alice think it so *very* much out of the way to hear the Rabbit say to itself, "Oh dear! Oh dear! I shall be too late!" (when she thought it over afterwards, it occurred to her that she ought to have wondered at this but at this time it all seemed quite natural); but when the Rabbit actually *took a watch out of its waistcoat-pocket*, and looked at it, and then hurried on, Alice started to her feet, for it flashed across her mind that she had never before seen a rabbit with either a waistcoat-pocket, or a watch to take out of it, and, burning with curiosity, she ran across the field after it, and was just in time to see it pop down a large rabbit-hole under the hedge.

In another moment down went Alice after it, never once considering how in the world she was to get out again.

The rabbit-hole went straight on like a tunnel for some way, and then dipped suddenly down, so suddenly that Alice had not a moment to think about stopping herself before she found herself falling down what seemed to be a very deep well.

Either the well was very deep, or she fell very slowly, for she had plenty of time as she went down to look about her, and to wonder what was going to happen next. First, she tried to look down and make out what she was coming to, but it was too dark to see anything: then she looked at the sides of the well, and noticed that they were filled with cupboards and bookshelves: here and there she saw maps and pictures hung upon pegs. She took down a jar from one of the shelves as she passed; it was labelled "ORANGE MARMALADE," but to her great disappointment it was empty: she did not like to drop the jar for fear of killing somebody underneath, so managed to put it into one of the cupboards as she fell past it.

"Well!" thought Alice to herself, "after such a fall as this, I shall think nothing of tumbling down stairs! How brave they'll all think me at home! Why, I wouldn't say anything about it, even if I fell off the top of the house!" (Which was very likely true.)

Down, down, down. Would the fall *never* come to an end? "I wonder how many miles I've fallen by this time?" she said aloud. "I must be getting somewhere near the centre of the earth. Let me see: that would be four thousand miles down, I think—" (for, you see, Alice had learnt several things of this sort in her lessons in the schoolroom, and though this was not a *very* good opportunity for showing off her knowledge, as there was no one to listen to her, still it was good practice to say it over) "—yes, that's about the right distance—but then I wonder what Latitude or Longitude I've got to?" (Alice had not the slightest idea what Latitude was, or Longitude either, but she thought they were nice grand words to say.)

Presently she began again. "I wonder if I shall fall right *through* the earth! How funny it'll seem to come out among the people that walk with their heads downwards! The Antipathies, I think—" (she was rather glad there *was* no one listening, this time, as it didn't sound at all the right word) "—but I shall have to ask them what the name of the country is, you know. Please, Ma'am, is this New Zealand or Australia?" (and she tried to curtsey as she spoke— fancy *curtseying* as you're falling through the air! Do you think you could manage it?) "And what an ignorant little girl she'll think me for asking! No, it'll never do to ask: perhaps I shall see it written up somewhere."

Down, down, down. There was nothing else to do, so Alice soon began talking again. "Dinah'll miss me very much to-night, I should think!" (Dinah was the cat.) "I hope they'll remember her saucer of milk at tea-time. Dinah, my dear! I wish you were down here with me! There are no mice in the air, I'm afraid, but you might catch a bat, and that's very like a mouse, you know. But do cats eat bats, I wonder?" And here Alice began to get rather sleepy, and went on saying to herself, in a dreamy sort of way, "Do cats eat bats? Do cats eat bats?" and sometimes, "Do bats eat cats?" for, you see, as she couldn't answer either question, it didn't much matter which way she put it. She felt that she was dozing off, and had just begun to dream that she was walking hand in hand with Dinah, and was saying to her very earnestly, "Now, Dinah, tell me the truth: did you ever eat a bat?" when suddenly, thump! thump! down she came upon a heap of sticks and dry leaves, and the fall was over.

Alice was not a bit hurt, and she jumped up onto her feet in a moment: she looked up, but it was all dark overhead; before her was another long passage, and the White Rabbit was still in sight, hurrying down it. There was not a moment to be lost: away went Alice like the wind, and was just in time to hear it say, as it turned a corner, "Oh my ears and whiskers, how late it's getting!" She was close behind it when she turned the corner, but the Rabbit was no longer to be seen: she found herself in a long, low hall, which was lit up by a row of lamps hanging from the roof.

There were doors all round the hall, but they were all locked, and when Alice had been all the way down one side and up the other, trying every door, she walked sadly down the middle, wondering how she was ever to get out again.

Suddenly she came upon a little three-legged table, all made of solid glass; there was nothing on it but a tiny golden key, and Alice's first idea was that this might belong to one of the doors of the hall; but, alas! either the locks were too large, or the key was too small, but at any rate it would not open any of them. However, on the second time round, she came upon a low curtain she had not noticed before, and behind it was a little door about fifteen inches high: she tried the little golden key in the lock, and to her great delight it fitted!

Alice opened the door and found that it led into a small passage, not much larger than a rat-hole: she knelt down and looked along the passage into the loveliest garden you ever saw. How she longed to get

out of that dark hall, and wander about among those beds of bright flowers and those cool fountains, but she could not even get her head through the doorway; "And even if my head would go through," thought poor Alice, "it would be of very little use without my shoulders. Oh, how I wish I could shut up like a telescope! I think I could, if I only knew how to begin." For, you see, so many out-of-the-way things had happened lately, that Alice had begun to think that very few things indeed were really impossible.

There seemed to be no use in waiting by the little door, so she went back to the table, half hoping she might find another key on it, or at any rate a book of rules for shutting people up like telescopes: this time she found a little bottle on it ("Which certainly was not here before," said Alice) and tied round the neck of the bottle was a paper label, with the words "DRINK ME" beautifully printed on it in large letters.

It was all very well to say "Drink me," but the wise little Alice was not going to do *that* in a hurry. "No, I'll look first," she said, "and see whether it's marked 'poison' or not"; for she had read several nice little stories about children who had got burnt, and eaten up by wild beasts and other unpleasant things, all because they *would* not remember the simple rules their friends had taught them; such as, that a red-hot poker will burn you if you hold it too long; and that if you cut your finger *very* deeply with a knife, it usually bleeds;

and she had never forgotten that, if you drink much from a bottle marked "poison," it is almost certain to disagree with you, sooner or later.

However, this bottle was *not* marked "poison," so Alice ventured to taste it, and finding it very nice (it had, in fact, a sort of mixed flavour of cherry-tart, custard, pine-apple, roast turkey, toffy, and hot buttered toast), she very soon finished it off.

* * * * *

* * * *

* * * * *

"What a curious feeling!" said Alice; "I must be shutting up like a telescope."

And so it was indeed: she was now only ten inches high, and her face brightened up at the thought that she was now the right size for going through the little door into that lovely garden. First, however, she waited for a few minutes to see if she was going to shrink any further: she felt a little nervous about this; "For it might end, you know," said Alice to herself, "in my going out altogether, like a candle. I wonder what I should be like then?" And she tried to fancy what the flame of a candle looks like after the candle is blown out, for she could not remember ever having seen such a thing.

After a while, finding that nothing more happened, she decided on going into the garden at once; but, alas for poor Alice! when she got to the door, she found she had forgotten the little golden key, and when she went back to the table for it, she found she could not possibly reach it: she could see it quite plainly through the glass, and she tried her best to climb up one of the legs of the table, but it was too slippery; and when she had tired herself out with trying, the poor little thing sat down and cried.

"Come, there's no use in crying like that!" said Alice to herself, rather sharply; "I advise you to leave off this minute!" She generally gave herself very good advice (though she very seldom followed it), and sometimes she scolded herself so severely as to bring tears into her eyes; and once she remembered trying to box her own ears for having cheated herself in a game of croquet she was playing against herself, for this curious child was very fond of pretending to be two people. "But it's no use now," thought poor Alice, "to pretend to be two people! Why, there's hardly enough of me left to make *one* respectable person!"

Soon her eye fell on a little glass box that was lying under the table: she opened it, and found in it a very small cake, on which the words "EAT ME" were beautifully marked in currants. "Well, I'll eat it," said Alice, "and if it makes me grow larger, I can reach the key; and if it makes me grow smaller, I can creep under the door; so either way I'll get into the garden, and I don't care which happens!"

She ate a little bit, and said anxiously to herself, "Which way? Which way?" holding her hand on the top of her head to feel which way it was growing, and she was quite surprised to find that she remained the same size: to be sure, this is what generally happens when one eats cake, but Alice had got so much into the way of expecting nothing but out-of-the-way things to happen, that it seemed quite dull and stupid for life to go on in the common way.

So she set to work, and very soon finished off the cake.

*   *   *   *   *

*   *   *   *

*   *   *   *   *

CHAPTER II

THE POOL OF TEARS

"Curiouser and curiouser!" cried Alice (she was so much surprised, that for the moment she quite forgot how to speak good English); "now I'm opening out like the largest telescope that ever was! Good-bye, feet!" (For when she 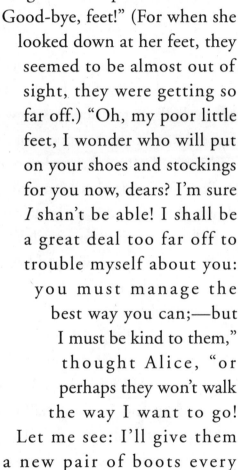 looked down at her feet, they seemed to be almost out of sight, they were getting so far off.) "Oh, my poor little feet, I wonder who will put on your shoes and stockings for you now, dears? I'm sure *I* shan't be able! I shall be a great deal too far off to trouble myself about you: you must manage the best way you can;—but I must be kind to them," thought Alice, "or perhaps they won't walk the way I want to go! Let me see: I'll give them a new pair of boots every Christmas."

And she went on planning to herself how she would manage it. "They must go by the carrier," she thought; "and how funny it'll seem, sending presents to one's own feet! And how odd the directions will look!

> *Alice's Right Foot, Esq.*
> *Hearthrug,*
> > *near the Fender,*
> > > *(with Alice's love.)*

Oh dear, what nonsense I'm talking!"

Just at this moment her head struck against the roof of the hall: in fact she was now rather more than nine feet high, and she at once took up the little golden key and hurried off to the garden door.

Poor Alice! It was as much as she could do, lying down on one side, to look through into the garden with one eye; but to get through was more hopeless than ever: she sat down and began to cry again.

"You ought to be ashamed of yourself," said Alice, "a great girl like you" (she might well say this), "to go on crying in this way! Stop this moment, I tell you!" But she went on all the same, shedding gallons of tears, until there was a large pool all round her, about four inches deep and reaching half down the hall.

After a time she heard a little pattering of feet in the distance, and she hastily dried her eyes to see what was coming. It was the White Rabbit returning, splendidly dressed, with a pair of white kid gloves in one hand

and a large fan in the other: he came trotting along in a great hurry, muttering to himself as he came, "Oh! the Duchess, the Duchess! Oh! won't she be savage if I've kept her waiting!" Alice felt so desperate that she was ready to ask help of anyone; so, when the Rabbit came near her, she began, in a low, timid voice, "If you please, sir—" The Rabbit started violently, dropped the white kid gloves and the fan, and scurried away into the darkness as hard as he could go.

Alice took up the fan and gloves, and, as the hall was very hot, she kept fanning herself all the time she went on talking: "Dear, dear! How queer everything is to-day! And yesterday things went on just as usual. I wonder if I've been changed in the night? Let me think: was I the same when I got up this morning? I almost think I can remember feeling a little different. But if I'm not the same, the next question is, Who in the world am I? Ah, *that's* the great puzzle!" And she began thinking over all the children she knew, that were of the same age as herself, to see if she could have been changed for any of them.

"I'm sure I'm not Ada," she said, "for her hair goes in such long ringlets, and mine doesn't go in ringlets at all; and I'm sure I can't be Mabel, for I know all sorts of things, and she, oh! she knows such a very little! Besides, *she's* she, and *I'm* I, and—oh dear, how puzzling it all is! I'll try if I know all the things I used to know. Let me see: four times five is twelve, and four times six is thirteen, and four times seven is—oh dear! I shall never get to twenty at that rate! However, the Multiplication Table doesn't signify: let's try Geography. London is the capital of Paris, and Paris is the capital of Rome, and Rome—no, *that's* all wrong, I'm certain! I must have been changed for Mabel! I'll try and say *'How doth the little—'*" and she crossed her hands on her lap as if she were saying lessons, and began to repeat it, but her voice sounded hoarse

166

and strange, and the words did not come the same as they used to do:

"How doth the little crocodile
Improve his shining tail,
And pour the waters of the Nile
On every golden scale!

"How cheerfully he seems to grin,
How neatly spreads his claws,
And welcomes little fishes in
With gently smiling jaws!"

"I'm sure those are not the right words," said poor Alice, and her eyes filled with tears again as she went on, "I must be Mabel after all, and I shall have to go and live in that poky little house, and have next to no toys to play with, and oh! ever so many lessons to learn! No, I've made up my mind about it; if I'm Mabel, I'll stay down here! It'll be no use their putting their heads down and saying, 'Come up again, dear!' I shall only look up and say, 'Who am I then? Tell me that first, and then, if I like being that person, I'll come up: if not I'll stay down here till I'm somebody else'—but, oh dear!" cried Alice with a sudden burst of tears, "I do wish they *would* put their heads down! I am so *very* tired of being all alone here!"

As she said this she looked down at her hands, and was surprised to see that she had put on one of the

Rabbit's little white kid gloves while she was talking. "How *can* I have done that?" she thought. "I must be growing small again." She got up and went to the table to measure herself by it, and found that, as nearly as she could guess, she was now about two feet high, and was going on shrinking rapidly: she soon found out that the cause of this was the fan she was holding, and she dropped it hastily, just in time to save herself from shrinking away altogether.

"That *was* a narrow escape!" said Alice, a good deal frightened at the sudden change, but very glad to find herself still in existence; "and now for the garden!" and she ran with all speed back to the little door: but alas! the little door was shut again, and the little golden key was lying on the glass table as before, "And things are worse than ever," thought the poor child, "for I never was so small as this before, never! And I declare it's too bad, that it is!"

As she said these words her foot slipped, and in another moment, splash! she was up to her chin in salt water. Her first idea was that she had somehow fallen into the sea, "And in that case I can go back by railway," she said to herself. (Alice had been to the seaside once in her life, and had come to the general conclusion, that wherever you go to on the English coast you find a number of bathing machines in the sea, some children digging in the sand with wooden spades, then a row of lodging houses, and behind them a railway station.) However she soon made out that she was in the pool of tears which she had wept when she was nine feet high.

"I wish I hadn't cried so much!" said Alice, as she swam about, trying to find her way out. "I shall be punished for it now, I suppose, by being drowned in my own tears! That *will* be a queer thing, to be sure! However, everything is queer to-day."

Just then she heard something splashing about in the pool a little way off, and she swam nearer to make out what it was: at first she thought it must be a walrus or hippopotamus, but then she remembered how small she was now, and she soon made out that it was only a mouse that had slipped in like herself.

"Would it be of any use, now," thought Alice, "to speak to this mouse? Everything is so out-of-the-way down here, that I should think very likely it can talk: at any rate there's no harm in trying." So she began: "O Mouse, do you know the way out of this pool? I am very tired of swimming about here, O Mouse!" (Alice thought this must be the right way of speaking to a mouse: she had never done such a thing before, but she remembered having seen in her brother's Latin Grammar, "A mouse—of a mouse—to a mouse—a mouse—O mouse!") The Mouse looked at her rather inquisitively, and seemed to her to wink with one of its little eyes, but it said nothing.

"Perhaps it doesn't understand English," thought Alice; "I daresay it's a French mouse, come over with William the Conqueror." (For, with all her knowledge of history, Alice had no very clear notion how long ago anything had happened.) So she began again: "Où est ma chatte?"* which was the first sentence in her French lesson-book. The Mouse gave a sudden leap out of the water, and seemed to quiver all over with fright. "Oh, I beg your pardon!" cried Alice hastily, afraid that she had hurt the poor animal's feelings. "I quite forgot you didn't like cats."

"Not like cats!" cried the Mouse, in a shrill, passionate voice. "Would *you* like cats if you were me?"

"Well, perhaps not," said Alice in a soothing tone: "don't be angry about it. And yet I wish I could show you our cat Dinah: I think you'd take a fancy to cats if you could only see her. She is such a dear quiet thing," Alice went on, half to herself, as she swam lazily about in the pool, "and she sits purring so nicely by the fire, licking her paws and washing her face—and she is such a nice soft thing to nurse—and she's such a capital one

---

* *"Where is my cat?"*

for catching mice—oh, I beg your pardon!" cried Alice again, for this time the Mouse was bristling all over, and she felt certain it must be really offended. "We won't talk about her any more if you'd rather not."

"We, indeed!" cried the Mouse, who was trembling down to the end of his tail. "As if *I* would talk on such a subject! Our family always *hated* cats: nasty, low, vulgar things! Don't let me hear the name again!"

"I won't indeed!" said Alice, in a great hurry to change the subject of conversation. "Are you—are you fond—of—of dogs?" The mouse did not answer; so Alice went on eagerly: "There is such a nice little dog near our house I should like to show you! A little bright-eyed terrier, you know, with oh! such long curly brown hair! And it'll fetch things when you throw them, and it'll sit up and beg for its dinner, and all sorts of things—I can't remember half of them—and it belongs to a farmer, you know, and he says it's so useful, it's worth a hundred pounds! He says it kills all the rats and—oh dear!" cried Alice in a sorrowful tone. "I'm afraid I've offended it again!" For the Mouse was swimming away from her as hard as it could go, and making quite a commotion in the pool as it went.

So she called softly after it: "Mouse dear! Do come back again, and we won't talk about cats or dogs either, if you don't like them!" When the Mouse heard this, it turned round and swam slowly back to her: its face was quite pale (with passion, Alice thought), and it said in a low, trembling voice, "Let us get to the shore, and then I'll tell you my history, and you'll understand why it is I hate cats and dogs."

It was high time to go, for the pool was getting quite crowded with the birds and animals that had fallen into it: there was a Duck and a Dodo, a Lory and an Eaglet, and several other curious creatures. Alice led the way, and the whole party swam to the shore.

Alice and the animals dry themselves off by running chaotically around in a "caucus race." The mouse tries to relate his history, but when Alice mentions her beloved Dinah, all the creatures are frightened away, leaving her, once again, alone.

The White Rabbit reappears, and mistaking Alice for one of his housemaids, bids her to fetch him some gloves. Obediently, Alice does what she is told. But once in his house, she again drinks from a mysterious bottle. This time Alice grows so large that she becomes stuck in the room, and not until she swallows some cake, which the Rabbit has thrown through the window, does she shrink enough to make her escape into a thick wood. Alice soon comes upon a large blue caterpillar sitting on top of a mushroom, smoking a long hookah, "and taking not the smallest notice of her or of anything else."

CHAPTER V

ADVICE FROM A CATERPILLAR

The Caterpillar and Alice looked at each other for some time in silence: at last the Caterpillar took the hookah out of its mouth, and addressed her in a languid, sleepy voice.

"Who are *you?*" said the Caterpillar.

This was not an encouraging opening for a conversation. Alice replied, rather shyly, "I—I hardly know, sir, just at present—at least I know who I *was* when I got up this morning, but I think I must have been changed several times since then."

"What do you mean by that?" said the Caterpillar sternly. "Explain yourself!"

"I can't explain *myself,* I'm afraid, sir," said Alice, "because I'm not myself, you see."

"I don't see," said the Caterpillar.

"I'm afraid I can't put it more clearly," Alice replied very politely, "for I can't understand it myself to begin with; and being so many different sizes in a day is very confusing."

"It isn't," said the Caterpillar.

"Well, perhaps you haven't found it so yet," said Alice; "but when you have to turn into a chrysalis— you will someday, you know—and then after that into a butterfly, I should think you'll feel it a little queer, won't you?"

"Not a bit," said the Caterpillar.

"Well, perhaps your feelings may be different," said Alice; "all I know is, it would feel very queer to *me*."

"You!" said the Caterpillar contemptuously. "Who are *you*?"

Which brought them back again to the beginning of the conversation. Alice felt a little irritated at the Caterpillar's making such *very* short remarks, and she drew herself up and said, very gravely, "I think you ought to tell me who *you* are, first."

"Why?" said the Caterpillar.

Here was another puzzling question; and, as Alice could not think of any good reason, and as the Caterpillar seemed to be in a *very* unpleasant state of mind, she turned away.

"Come back!" the Caterpillar called after her. "I've something important to say!"

This sounded promising, certainly: Alice turned and came back again.

"Keep your temper," said the Caterpillar.

"Is that all?" said Alice, swallowing down her anger as well as she could.

"No," said the Caterpillar.

Alice thought she might as well wait, as she had nothing else to do, and perhaps after all it might tell her something worth hearing. For some minutes it puffed away without speaking, but at last it unfolded its arms, took the hookah out of its mouth again, and said, "So you think you're changed, do you?"

"I'm afraid I am, sir," said Alice; "I can't remember things as I used—and I don't keep the same size for ten minutes together!"

"Can't remember *what* things?" said the Caterpillar.

"Well, I've tried to say 'How doth the little busy bee,' but it all came different!" Alice replied in a very melancholy voice.

"Repeat '*You are old, Father William,*' " said the Caterpillar.

Alice folded her hands, and began:

"You are old, Father William," the young man said,
 "And your hair has become very white;
And yet you incessantly stand on your head—
 Do you think, at your age, it is right?"

"In my youth," Father William replied to his son,
 "I feared it might injure the brain;
But now that I'm perfectly sure I have none,
 Why, I do it again and again."

"You are old," said the youth, "as I mentioned before,
And have grown most uncommonly fat;
Yet you turned a back-somersault in at the door—
Pray, what is the reason of that?"

"In my youth," said the sage, as he shook his grey locks,
"I kept all my limbs very supple
By the use of this ointment—one shilling the box—
Allow me to sell you a couple."

"You are old," said the youth, "and your jaws are too weak
 For anything tougher than suet;
Yet you finished the goose, with the bones and the beak—
 Pray, how did you manage to do it?"

"In my youth," said his father, "I took to the law,
 And argued each case with my wife;
And the muscular strength, which it gave to my jaw,
 Has lasted the rest of my life."

"You are old," said the youth; "one would hardly suppose
  That your eye was as steady as ever;
Yet you balanced an eel on the end of your nose—
  What made you so awfully clever?"

"I have answered three questions, and that is enough,"
  Said his father; "don't give yourself airs!
Do you think I can listen all day to such stuff?
  Be off, or I'll kick you down stairs!"

"That is not said right," said the Caterpillar.

"Not *quite* right, I'm afraid," said Alice timidly; "some of the words have got altered."

"It is wrong from beginning to end," said the Caterpillar decidedly, and there was silence for some minutes.

The Caterpillar was the first to speak.

"What size do you want to be?" it asked.

"Oh, I'm not particular as to size," Alice hastily replied; "only one doesn't like changing so often, you know."

"I *don't* know," said the Caterpillar.

Alice said nothing: she had never been so much contradicted in all her life before, and she felt that she was losing her temper.

"Are you content now?" said the Caterpillar.

"Well, I should like to be a *little* larger, sir, if you wouldn't mind," said Alice: "three inches is such a wretched height to be."

"It is a very good height indeed!" said the Caterpillar angrily, rearing itself upright as it spoke (it was exactly three inches high).

"But I'm not used to it!" pleaded poor Alice in a piteous tone. And she thought to herself, "I wish the creatures wouldn't be so easily offended."

"You'll get used to it in time," said the Caterpillar; and it put the hookah into its mouth and began smoking again.

This time Alice waited patiently until it chose to speak again. In a minute or two the Caterpillar took the hookah out of its mouth and yawned once or twice, and shook itself. Then it got down off the mushroom, and crawled away into the grass, merely remarking as it went, "One side will make you grow taller, and the other side will make you grow shorter."

"One side of *what*? The other side of *what*?" thought Alice to herself.

"Of the mushroom," said the Caterpillar, just as if she had asked it aloud; and in another moment it was out of sight.

Alice remained looking thoughtfully at the mushroom for a minute, trying to make out which were the two sides of it; and, as it was perfectly round, she found this a very difficult question. However, at last she stretched her arms round it as far as they would go, and broke off a bit of the edge with each hand.

"And now which is which?" she said to herself, and nibbled a little of the right-hand bit to try the effect: the next moment she felt a violent blow underneath her chin; it had struck her foot!

She was a good deal frightened by this very sudden change, but she felt that there was no time to be lost, as she was shrinking rapidly; so she set to work at once to eat some of the other bit. Her chin was pressed so closely against her foot, that there was hardly room to open her mouth; but she did it at last, and managed to swallow a morsel of the left-hand bit.

*   *   *   *   *
*   *   *   *
*   *   *   *   *

"Come, my head's free at last!" said Alice in a tone of delight, which changed into alarm in another moment, when she found that her shoulders were nowhere to be found: all she could see when she looked down, was an immense length of neck, which seemed to rise like a stalk out of a sea of green leaves that lay far below her.

"What *can* all that green stuff be?" said Alice. "And where *have* my shoulders got to? And oh, my poor hands, how is it I can't see you?" She was moving them about as she spoke, but no result seemed to follow, except a little shaking among the distant green leaves.

As there seemed to be no chance of getting her hands up to her head, she tried to get her head down to them, and was delighted to find that her neck would bend about easily in any direction, like a serpent. She had just succeeded in curving it down into a graceful zigzag, and was going to dive in among the leaves, which she found to be nothing but the tops of the trees under which she had been wandering, when a sharp hiss made her draw back in a hurry: a large pigeon had flown into her face, and was beating her violently with its wings.

"Serpent!" screamed the Pigeon.

"I'm *not* a serpent!" said Alice indignantly. "Let me alone!"

"Serpent, I say again!" repeated the Pigeon, but in a more subdued tone, and added with a kind of sob, "I've tried every way, and nothing seems to suit them!"

"I haven't the least idea what you're talking about," said Alice.

"I've tried the roots of trees, and I've tried banks, and I've tried hedges," the Pigeon went on, without attending to her; "but those serpents! There's no pleasing them!"

Alice was more and more puzzled, but she thought there was no use in saying anything more till the Pigeon had finished.

"As if it wasn't trouble enough hatching the eggs," said the Pigeon, "but I must be on the look-out for serpents night and day! Why, I haven't had a wink of sleep these three weeks!"

"I'm very sorry you've been annoyed," said Alice, who was beginning to see its meaning.

"And just as I'd taken the highest tree in the wood," continued the Pigeon, raising its voice to a shriek, "and just as I was thinking I should be free of them at last, they must needs come wriggling down from the sky! Ugh! Serpent!"

"But I'm *not* a serpent, I tell you!" said Alice, "I'm a—I'm a—"

"Well! *What* are you?" said the Pigeon. "I can see you're trying to invent something!"

"I—I'm a little girl," said Alice, rather doubtfully, as she remembered the number of changes she had gone through that day.

"A likely story indeed!" said the Pigeon in a tone of the deepest contempt. "I've seen a good many little girls in my time, but never *one* with such a neck as that! No, no! You're a serpent; and there's no use denying it. I suppose you'll be telling me next that you never tasted an egg!"

"I *have* tasted eggs, certainly," said Alice, who was a very truthful child; "but little girls eat eggs quite as much as serpents do, you know."

"I don't believe it," said the Pigeon; "but if they do, why then they're a kind of serpent, that's all I can say."

This was such a new idea to Alice, that she was quite silent for a minute or two, which gave the Pigeon the opportunity of adding, "You're looking for eggs, I know *that* well enough; and what does it matter to me whether you're a little girl or a serpent?"

"It matters a good deal to *me*," said Alice hastily; "but I'm not looking for eggs, as it happens; and if I was, I shouldn't want *yours:* I don't like them raw."

"Well, be off, then!" said the Pigeon in a sulky tone, as it settled down again into its nest. Alice crouched

185

down among the trees as well as she could, for her neck kept getting entangled among the branches, and every now and then she had to stop and untwist it. After a while she remembered that she still held the pieces of mushroom in her hands, and she set to work very carefully, nibbling first at one and then at the other, and growing sometimes taller and sometimes shorter, until she had succeeded in bringing herself down to her usual height.

It was so long since she had been anything near the right size, that it felt quite strange at first, but she got used to it in a few minutes, and began talking to herself as usual. "Come, there's half my plan done now! How puzzling all these changes are! I'm never sure what I'm going to be, from one minute to another! However, I've got back to my right size: the next thing is, to get into that beautiful garden—how *is* that to be done, I wonder?" As she said this, she came suddenly upon an open place, with a little house in it about four feet high. "Whoever lives there," thought Alice, "it'll never do to come upon them *this* size: why, I should frighten them out of their wits!" So she began nibbling at the right-hand bit again, and did not venture to go near the house till she had brought herself down to nine inches high.

CHAPTER VI

PIG AND PEPPER

As Alice watches the house, wondering what to do next, a footman, with the face of a fish, approaches and knocks on the door. A Frog-Footman answers and receives the message: "For the Duchess. An invitation from the Queen to play croquet." Following this exchange, Alice goes up to the house and has a frustrating conversation with the Frog-Footman, who doesn't seem eager to help her to enter.

"Oh, there's no use in talking to him," said Alice desperately. "He's perfectly idiotic!" And she opened the door and went in.

The door led right into a large kitchen, which was full of smoke from one end to the other: the Duchess was sitting on a three-legged stool in the middle, nursing a baby; the cook was leaning over the fire, stirring a large cauldron which seemed to be full of soup.

"There's certainly too much pepper in that soup!" Alice said to herself, as well as she could for sneezing.

There was certainly too much of it in the air. Even the Duchess sneezed occasionally; and as for the baby, it was sneezing and howling alternately without a moment's pause. The only two creatures in the kitchen that did not sneeze were the cook and a large cat which was sitting on the hearth and grinning from ear to ear.

"Please, would you tell me," said Alice, a little timidly, for she was not quite sure whether it was good manners for her to speak first, "why your cat grins like that?"

"It's a Cheshire cat," said the Duchess, "and that's why. Pig!"

She said the last word with such sudden violence that Alice quite jumped; but she saw in another moment that it was addressed to the baby, and not to her, so she took courage, and went on again—

"I didn't know that Cheshire cats always grinned; in fact, I didn't know that cats *could* grin."

"They all can," said the Duchess; "and most of 'em do."

"I don't know of any that do," Alice said very politely, feeling quite pleased to have got into a conversation.

"You don't know much," said the Duchess; "and that's a fact."

Alice did not at all like the tone of this remark, and thought it would be as well to introduce some other subject of conversation. While she was trying to fix on one, the cook took the cauldron of soup off the fire, and at once set to work throwing everything within her reach at the Duchess and the baby—the fire-irons came first; then followed a shower of saucepans, plates, and dishes. The Duchess took no notice of them even when they hit her; and the baby was howling so much already, that it was quite impossible to say whether the blows hurt it or not.

"Oh, *please* mind what you're doing!" cried Alice, jumping up and down in an agony of terror. "Oh, there goes his *precious* nose!" as an unusually large saucepan flew close by it, and very nearly carried it off.

"If everybody minded their own business," said the Duchess in a hoarse growl, "the world would go round a deal faster than it does."

"Which would *not* be an advantage," said Alice, who felt very glad to get an opportunity of showing off a little of her knowledge. "Just think what work it would make with the day and night! You see the earth takes twenty-four hours to turn round on its axis—"

"Talking of axes," said the Duchess, "chop off her head!"

Alice glanced rather anxiously at the cook, to see if she meant to take the hint; but the cook was busily stirring the soup, and seemed not to be listening, so she went on again: "Twenty-four hours, I *think;* or is it twelve? I—"

"Oh, don't bother *me*," said the Duchess; "I never could abide figures!" And with that she began nursing her child again, singing a sort of lullaby to it as she did so, and giving it a violent shake at the end of every line:

"Speak roughly to your little boy,
And beat him when he sneezes;
He only does it to annoy,
Because he knows it teases."

CHORUS

(In which the cook and the baby joined)

"Wow! wow! wow!"

While the Duchess sang the second verse of the song, she kept tossing the baby violently up and down, and the poor little thing howled so, that Alice could hardly hear the words:

"I speak severely to my boy,
I beat him when he sneezes;
For he can thoroughly enjoy
The pepper when he pleases!"

CHORUS

"Wow! wow! wow!"

"Here! you may nurse it a bit, if you like!" said the Duchess to Alice, flinging the baby at her as she spoke. "I must go and get ready to play croquet with the Queen," and she hurried out of the room. The cook threw a frying-pan after her as she went, but it just missed her.

Alice caught the baby with some difficulty, as it was a queer-shaped little creature, and held out its arms and legs in all directions, "Just like a star-fish," thought Alice. The poor little thing was snorting like a steam-engine when she caught it, and kept doubling itself up and straightening itself out again, so that altogether, for the first minute or two, it was as much as she could do to hold it.

As soon as she had made out the proper way of nursing it (which was to twist it up into a sort of knot, and then keep tight hold of its right ear and left foot, so as to prevent its undoing itself), she carried it out into the open air. "If I don't take this child away with me," thought Alice, "they're sure to kill it in a day or two: wouldn't it be murder to leave it behind?" She said the last words out loud, and the little thing grunted in reply (it had left off sneezing by this time). "Don't grunt," said Alice; "that's not at all a proper way of expressing yourself."

The baby grunted again, and Alice looked very anxiously into its face to see what was the matter with it. There could be no doubt that it had a *very* turn-up nose, much more like a snout than a real nose; also its eyes were getting extremely small for a baby: altogether Alice did not like the look of the thing at all. "But perhaps it was only sobbing," she thought, and looked into its eyes again, to see if there were any tears.

No, there were no tears. "If you're going to turn into a pig, my dear," said Alice, seriously, "I'll have nothing more to do with you. Mind now!" The poor little thing sobbed again (or grunted, it was impossible to say which), and they went on for some while in silence.

Alice was just beginning to think to herself, "Now, what am I to do with this creature when I get it

home?" when it grunted again, so violently, that she looked down into its face in some alarm. This time there could be *no* mistake about it: it was neither more nor less than a pig, and she felt that it would be quite absurd for her to carry it any further.

So she set the little creature down, and felt quite relieved to see it trot away quietly into the wood. "If it had grown up," she said to herself, "it would have made a dreadfully ugly child: but it makes rather a handsome pig, I think." And she began thinking over other children she knew, who might do very well as pigs, and was just saying to herself, "If one only knew the right way to change them—" when she was a little startled by seeing the Cheshire Cat sitting on a bough of a tree a few yards off.

The Cat only grinned when it saw Alice. It looked good-natured, she thought: still it had *very* long claws and a great many teeth, so she felt it ought to be treated with respect.

"Cheshire Puss," she began, rather timidly, as she did not at all know whether it would like the name: however, it only grinned a little wider. "Come, it's pleased so far," thought Alice, and she went on, "Would you tell me, please, which way I ought to walk from here?"

"That depends a good deal on where you want to get to," said the Cat.

"I don't much care where—" said Alice.

"Then it doesn't matter which way you walk," said the Cat.

"—so long as I get *somewhere*," Alice added as an explanation.

"Oh, you're sure to do that," said the Cat, "if you only walk long enough."

Alice felt that this could not be denied, so she tried another question. "What sort of people live about here?"

"In *that* direction," the Cat said, waving its right paw round, "lives a Hatter: and in *that* direction," waving the other paw, "lives a March Hare. Visit either you like: they're both mad."

195

"But I don't want to go among mad people," Alice remarked.

"Oh, you can't help that," said the Cat: "we're all mad here. I'm mad. You're mad."

"How do you know I'm mad?" said Alice.

"You must be," said the Cat, "or you wouldn't have come here."

Alice didn't think that proved it at all; however, she went on: "And how do you know that you're mad?"

"To begin with," said the Cat, "a dog's not mad. You grant that?"

"I suppose so," said Alice.

"Well then," the Cat went on, "you see a dog growls when it's angry, and wags its tail when it's pleased. Now *I* growl when I'm pleased, and wag my tail when I'm angry. Therefore I'm mad."

"*I* call it purring, not growling," said Alice.

"Call it what you like," said the Cat. "Do you play croquet with the Queen to-day?"

"I should like it very much," said Alice, "but I haven't been invited yet."

"You'll see me there," said the Cat, and vanished.

Alice was not much surprised at this, she was getting so well used to queer things happening. While she was still looking at the place where it had been, it suddenly appeared again.

"By-the-bye, what became of the baby?" said the Cat. "I'd nearly forgotten to ask."

"It turned into a pig," Alice answered very quietly, just as if the Cat had come back in a natural way.

"I thought it would," said the Cat, and vanished again.

Alice waited a little, half expecting to see it again, but it did not appear, and after a minute or two she walked on in the direction in which the March Hare was said to live. "I've seen hatters before," she said to herself: "the March Hare will be much the most interesting, and perhaps as this is May it won't be raving mad—at least not so mad as it was in March." As she said this, she looked up, and there was the Cat again, sitting on a branch of a tree.

"Did you say pig, or fig?" said the Cat.

"I said pig," replied Alice; "and I wish you wouldn't keep appearing and vanishing so suddenly: you make one quite giddy."

"All right," said the Cat; and this time it vanished quite slowly, beginning with the end of the tail, and ending with the grin, which remained some time after the rest of it had gone.

"Well! I've often seen a cat without a grin," thought Alice; "but a grin without a cat! It's the most curious thing I ever saw in all my life!"

She had not gone much farther before she came in sight of the house of the March Hare: she thought it must be the right house, because the chimneys were shaped like ears and the roof was thatched with fur. It was so large a house, that she did not like to go nearer till she had nibbled some more of the left-hand bit of mushroom, and raised herself to about two feet high: even then she walked up towards it rather timidly, saying to herself, "Suppose it should be raving mad after all! I almost wish I'd gone to see the Hatter instead!"

ALICE'S ADVENTURES IN WONDERLAND

Lewis Carroll

CHAPTER VII

A MAD TEA-PARTY

There was a table set out under a tree in front of the house, and the March Hare and the Hatter were having tea at it. A Dormouse was sitting between them, fast asleep, and the other two were using it as a cushion, resting their elbows on it, and talking over its head. "Very uncomfortable for the Dormouse," thought Alice; "only, as it's asleep, I suppose it doesn't mind."

The table was a large one, but the three were all crowded together at one corner of it: "No room! No room!" they cried out when they saw Alice coming. "There's *plenty* of room!" said Alice indignantly, and she sat down in a large arm-chair at one end of the table.

"Have some wine," the March Hare said in an encouraging tone.

Alice looked all round the table, but there was nothing on it but tea. "I don't see any wine," she remarked.

"There isn't any," said the March Hare.

"Then it wasn't very civil of you to offer it," said Alice angrily.

"It wasn't very civil of you to sit down without being invited," said the March Hare.

"I didn't know it was *your* table," said Alice; "it's laid for a great many more than three."

"Your hair wants cutting," said the Hatter. He had been looking at Alice for some time with great curiosity, and this was his first speech.

"You should learn not to make personal remarks," Alice said with some severity: "it's very rude."

The Hatter opened his eyes very wide on hearing this; but all he *said* was, "Why is a raven like a writing-desk?"

"Come, we shall have some fun now!" thought Alice. "I'm glad they've begun asking riddles—I believe I can guess that," she added aloud.

"Do you mean that you think you can find out the answer to it?" said the March Hare.

"Exactly so," said Alice.

"Then you should say what you mean," the March Hare went on.

"I do," Alice hastily replied; "at least—at least I mean what I say—that's the same thing, you know."

"Not the same thing a bit!" said the Hatter. "Why, you might just as well say that 'I see what I eat' is the same thing as 'I eat what I see'!"

"You might just as well say," added the March Hare, "that 'I like what I get' is the same thing as 'I get what I like'!"

"You might just as well say," added the Dormouse, who seemed to be talking in his sleep, "that 'I breathe when I sleep' is the same thing as 'I sleep when I breathe'!"

"It *is* the same thing with you," said the Hatter, and here the conversation dropped, and the party sat silent for a minute, while Alice thought over all she could remember about ravens and writing-desks, which wasn't much.

The Hatter was the first to break the silence. "What day of the month is it?" he said, turning to Alice: he had taken his watch out of his pocket, and was looking at it uneasily, shaking it every now and then, and holding it to his ear.

Alice considered a little, and said, "The fourth."

"Two days wrong!" sighed the Hatter. "I told you butter wouldn't suit the works!" he added, looking angrily at the March Hare.

"It was the *best* butter," the March Hare meekly replied.

"Yes, but some crumbs must have got in as well," the Hatter grumbled: "you shouldn't have put it in with the bread-knife."

The March Hare took the watch and looked at it gloomily: then he dipped it into his cup of tea, and looked at it again: but he could think of nothing better to say than his first remark, "It was the *best* butter, you know."

Alice had been looking over his shoulder with some curiosity. "What a funny watch!" she remarked. "It tells the day of the month, and doesn't tell what o'clock it is!"

"Why should it?" muttered the Hatter. "Does *your* watch tell you what year it is?"

"Of course not," Alice replied very readily: "but that's because it stays the same year for such a long time together."

"Which is just the case with *mine*," said the Hatter.

Alice felt dreadfully puzzled. The Hatter's remark seemed to her to have no sort of meaning in it, and yet it was certainly English. "I don't quite understand you," she said, as politely as she could.

"The Dormouse is asleep again," said the Hatter, and he poured a little hot tea onto its nose.

The Dormouse shook its head impatiently, and said, without opening its eyes, "Of course, of course; just what I was going to remark myself."

"Have you guessed the riddle yet?" the Hatter said, turning to Alice again.

"No, I give it up," Alice replied: "what's the answer?"

"I haven't the slightest idea," said the Hatter.

"Nor I," said the March Hare.

Alice sighed wearily. "I think you might do something better with the time," she said, "than wasting it in asking riddles that have no answers."

"If you knew Time as well as I do," said the Hatter, "you wouldn't talk about wasting *it*. It's *him*."

"I don't know what you mean," said Alice.

"Of course you don't!" the Hatter said, tossing his head contemptuously. "I dare say you never even spoke to Time!"

"Perhaps not," Alice cautiously replied: "but I know I have to beat time when I learn music."

"Ah, that accounts for it," said the Hatter. "He won't stand beating. Now, if you only kept on good terms with him, he'd do almost anything you liked with the clock. For instance, suppose it were nine o'clock in the morning, just time to begin lessons: you'd only have to whisper a hint to Time, and round goes the clock in a twinkling! Half-past one, time for dinner!"

("I only wish it was," the March Hare said to itself in a whisper.)

"That would be grand, certainly," said Alice thoughtfully: "but then—I shouldn't be hungry for it, you know."

"Not at first, perhaps," said the Hatter: "but you could keep it to half-past one as long as you liked."

"Is that the way *you* manage?" Alice asked.

The Hatter shook his head mournfully. "Not I!" he replied. "We quarrelled last March—just before *he* went mad, you know—" (pointing with his teaspoon at the March Hare), "—it was at the great concert given by the Queen of Hearts, and I had to sing

> *'Twinkle, twinkle, little bat!*
> *How I wonder what you're at!'*

You know the song perhaps?"

"I've heard something like it," said Alice.

"It goes on you know," the Hatter continued, "in this way:

'Up above the world you fly,
Like a teatray in the sky.
Twinkle, twinkle—' "

Here the Dormouse shook itself, and began singing in its sleep, *"Twinkle, twinkle, twinkle, twinkle—"* and went on so long that they had to pinch it to make it stop.

"Well, I'd hardly finished the first verse," said the Hatter, "when the Queen bawled out 'He's murdering the time! Off with his head!'"

"How dreadfully savage!" exclaimed Alice.

"And ever since that," the Hatter went on in a mournful tone, "he won't do a thing I ask! It's always six o'clock now."

A bright idea came into Alice's head. "Is that the reason so many tea-things are put out here?" she asked.

"Yes, that's it," said the Hatter with a sigh: "it's always tea-time, and we've no time to wash the things between whiles."

"Then you keep moving round, I suppose?" said Alice.

"Exactly so," said the Hatter: "as the things get used up."

"But when you come to the beginning again?" Alice ventured to ask.

"Suppose we change the subject," the March Hare interrupted, yawning. "I'm getting tired of this. I vote the young lady tells us a story."

"I'm afraid I don't know one," said Alice, rather alarmed at the proposal.

"Then the Dormouse shall!" they both cried. "Wake up, Dormouse!" And they pinched it on both sides at once.

The Dormouse slowly opened his eyes. "I wasn't asleep," he said in a hoarse, feeble voice: "I heard every word you fellows were saying."

"Tell us a story!" said the March Hare.

"Yes, please do!" pleaded Alice.

"And be quick about it," added the Hatter, "or you'll be asleep again before it's done."

"'Once upon a time there were three little sisters," the Dormouse began in a great hurry; "and their names were Elsie, Lacie, and Tillie; and they lived at the bottom of a well—"

"What did they live on?" said Alice, who always took a great interest in questions of eating and drinking.

"They lived on treacle," said the Dormouse, after thinking a minute or two.

"They couldn't have done that, you know," Alice gently remarked: "they'd have been ill."

"So they were," said the Dormouse; "*very* ill."

Alice tried a little to fancy to herself what such an extraordinary way of living would be like, but it puzzled her too much, so she went on: "But why did they live at the bottom of a well?"

"Take some more tea," the March Hare said to Alice, very earnestly.

"I've had nothing yet," Alice replied in an offended tone, "so I can't take more."

"You mean you can't take *less*," said the Hatter: "it's very easy to take *more* than nothing."

"Nobody asked *your* opinion," said Alice.

"Who's making personal remarks now?" the Hatter asked triumphantly.

Alice did not quite know what to say to this: so she helped herself to some tea and bread-and-butter, and then turned to the Dormouse, and repeated her question. "Why did they live at the bottom of a well?"

The Dormouse again took a minute or two to think about it, and then said, "It was a treacle-well."

"There's no such thing!" Alice was beginning very angrily, but the Hatter and the March Hare went "Sh! sh!" and the Dormouse sulkily remarked, "If you can't be civil, you'd better finish the story for yourself."

"No, please go on!" Alice said very humbly: "I won't interrupt you again. I daresay there may be *one*."

"One, indeed!" said the Dormouse indignantly. However, he consented to go on. "And so these three little sisters—they were learning to draw, you know—"

"What did they draw?" said Alice, quite forgetting her promise.

"Treacle," said the Dormouse, without considering at all this time.

"I want a clean cup," interrupted the Hatter: "let's all move one place on."

He moved on as he spoke, and the Dormouse followed him: the March Hare moved into the Dormouse's place, and Alice rather unwillingly took the place of the March Hare. The Hatter was the only one who got any advantage from the change: and Alice was a good deal worse off than before, as the March Hare had just upset the milk-jug into his plate.

Alice did not wish to offend the Dormouse again, so she began very cautiously: "But I don't understand. Where did they draw the treacle from?"

"You can draw water out of a water-well," said the Hatter; "so I should think you could draw treacle out of a treacle-well—eh, stupid?"

"But they were *in* the well," Alice said to the Dormouse, not choosing to notice this last remark.

"Of course they were," said the Dormouse, "—well in."

This answer so confused poor Alice, that she let the Dormouse go on for some time without interrupting it.

"They were learning to draw," the Dormouse went on, yawning and rubbing its eyes, for it was getting very sleepy; "and they drew all manner of things— everything that begins with an M—"

"Why with an M?" said Alice.

"Why not?" said the March Hare.

Alice was silent.

The Dormouse had closed its eyes by this time, and was going off into a doze; but, on being pinched by the Hatter, it woke up again with a little shriek, and went on "—that begins with an M, such as mousetraps, and the moon, and memory, and muchness—you know you say things are 'much of a muchness'—did you ever see such a thing as a drawing of a muchness?"

"Really, now you ask me," said Alice, very much confused, "I don't think—"

"Then you shouldn't talk," said the Hatter.

This piece of rudeness was more than Alice could bear: she got up in great disgust, and walked off; the Dormouse fell asleep instantly, and neither of the others took the least notice of her going, though she

looked back once or twice, half hoping that they would call after her: the last time she saw them, they were trying to put the Dormouse into the teapot.

"At any rate I'll never go *there* again!" said Alice as she picked her way through the wood. "It's the stupidest tea-party I ever was at in all my life!"

Just as she said this, she noticed that one of the trees had a door leading right into it. "That's very curious!" she thought. "But everything's curious to-day. I think I may as well go in at once." And in she went.

Once more she found herself in the long hall, and close to the little glass table. "Now, I'll manage better this time," she said to herself, and began by taking the little golden key, and unlocking the door that led into the garden. Then she set to work nibbling at the mushroom (she had kept a piece of it in her pocket) till she was about a foot high: then she walked down the little passage: and *then*—she found herself at last in the beautiful garden, among the bright flower-beds and the cool fountains.

CHAPTER VIII

THE QUEEN'S CROQUET-GROUND

A large rose-tree stood near the entrance of the garden: the roses growing on it were white, but there were three gardeners at it, busily painting them red. Alice thought this a very curious thing, and she went nearer to watch them, and just as she came up to them she heard one of them say, "Look out now, Five! Don't go splashing paint over me like that!"

"I couldn't help it," said Five, in a sulky tone; "Seven jogged my elbow."

On which Seven looked up and said, "That's right, Five! Always lay the blame on others!"

"*You'd* better not talk!" said Five. "I heard the Queen say only yesterday you deserved to be beheaded!"

"What for?" said the one who had spoken first.

"That's none of *your* business, Two!" said Seven.

"Yes, it *is* his business!" said Five, "and I'll tell him—it was for bringing the cook tulip-roots instead of onions."

Seven flung down his brush, and had just begun, "Well, of all the unjust things—" when his eye chanced to fall upon Alice, as she stood watching them, and he checked himself suddenly: the others looked round also, and all of them bowed low.

"Would you tell me, please," said Alice, a little timidly, "why you are painting those roses?"

Five and Seven said nothing, but looked at Two. Two began, in a low voice, "Why, the fact is, you see, Miss, this here ought to have been a *red* rose-tree, and we put a white one in by mistake, and if the Queen was to find it out, we should all have our heads cut off, you know. So you see, Miss, we're doing our best, afore she comes, to—" At this moment Five, who had been anxiously looking across the garden, called out, "The Queen! The Queen!" and the three gardeners instantly threw themselves flat upon their faces. There was a sound of many footsteps, and Alice looked round, eager to see the Queen.

First came ten soldiers carrying clubs; these were all shaped like the three gardeners, oblong and flat, with their hands and feet at the corners: next the ten courtiers; these were ornamented all over with diamonds, and walked two and two, as the soldiers did. After these came the royal children; there were ten of them, and the little dears came jumping merrily along hand in hand, in couples: they were all ornamented with hearts. Next came the guests, mostly Kings and

Queens, and among them Alice recognised the White Rabbit: it was talking in a hurried nervous manner, smiling at everything that was said, and went by without noticing her. Then followed the Knave of Hearts, carrying the King's crown on a crimson velvet cushion; and, last of all this grand procession, came THE KING AND QUEEN OF HEARTS.

Alice was rather doubtful whether she ought not to lie down on her face like the three gardeners, but she could not remember ever having heard of such a rule at processions; "And besides, what would be the use of a procession," she thought, "if people had all to lie down on their faces, so that they couldn't see it?" So she stood where she was, and waited.

When the procession came opposite to Alice, they all stopped and looked at her, and the Queen said severely, "Who is this?" She said it to the Knave of Hearts, who only bowed and smiled in reply.

"Idiot!" said the Queen, tossing her head impatiently; and, turning to Alice, she went on, "What's your name, child?"

"My name is Alice, so please your Majesty," said Alice very politely; but she added, to herself, "Why, they're only a pack of cards, after all. I needn't be afraid of them!"

"And who are *these*?" said the Queen, pointing to the three gardeners who were lying round the rose-tree; for you see, as they were lying on their faces, and the

213

pattern on their backs was the same as the rest of the pack, she could not tell whether they were gardeners, or soldiers, or courtiers, or three of her own children.

"How should *I* know?" said Alice, surprised at her own courage. "It's no business of *mine*."

The Queen turned crimson with fury, and, after glaring at her for a moment like a wild beast, began screaming, "Off with her head! Off—"

"Nonsense!" said Alice, very loudly and decidedly, and the Queen was silent.

The King laid his hand upon her arm, and timidly said, "Consider, my dear: she is only a child!"

The Queen turned angrily away from him, and said to the Knave, "Turn them over!"

The Knave did so, very carefully, with one foot.

"Get up!" said the Queen in a shrill, loud voice, and the three gardeners instantly jumped up, and began bowing to the King, the Queen, the royal children, and everybody else.

"Leave off that!" screamed the Queen. "You make me giddy." And then, turning to the rose-tree, she went on. "What *have* you been doing here?"

"May it please your Majesty," said Two, in a very humble tone, going down on one knee as he spoke, "we were trying—"

"*I* see!" said the Queen, who had meanwhile been examining the roses. "Off with their heads!" and the procession moved on, three of the soldiers remaining behind to execute the unfortunate gardeners, who ran to Alice for protection.

"You shan't be beheaded!" said Alice, and she put them into a large flower-pot that stood near. The three soldiers wandered about for a minute or two, looking for them, and then quietly marched off after the others.

"Are the heads off?" shouted the Queen.

"Their heads are gone, if it please your Majesty!" the soldiers shouted in reply.

215

"That's right!" shouted the Queen. "Can you play croquet?"

The soldiers were silent, and looked at Alice, as the question was evidently meant for her.

"Yes!" shouted Alice.

"Come on then!" roared the Queen, and Alice joined the procession, wondering very much what would happen next.

"It's—it's a very fine day!" said a timid voice at her side. She was walking by the White Rabbit, who was peeping anxiously into her face.

"Very," said Alice, "—where's the Duchess?"

"Hush! Hush!" said the Rabbit in a low, hurried tone. He looked anxiously over his shoulder as he spoke, and then raised himself upon tiptoe, put his mouth close to her ear, and whispered, "She's under sentence of execution."

"What for?" said Alice.

"Did you say, 'What a pity!'?" the Rabbit asked.

"No, I didn't," said Alice: "I don't think it's at all a pity. I said, 'What for?' "

"She boxed the Queen's ears—" the Rabbit began. Alice gave a little scream of laughter. "Oh, hush!" the Rabbit whispered in a frightened tone. "The Queen will hear you! You see she came rather late, and the Queen said—"

"Get to your places!" shouted the Queen in a voice of thunder, and people began running about in all directions, tumbling up against each other: however, they got settled down in a minute or two, and the game began.

Alice thought she had never seen such a curious croquet-ground in her life: it was all ridges and furrows; the croquet-balls were live hedgehogs, and the mallets live flamingoes, and the soldiers had to double themselves up and stand on their hands and feet, to make the arches.

The chief difficulty Alice found at first was in managing her flamingo: she succeeded in getting its body tucked away, comfortably enough, under her arm, with its legs hanging down, but generally, just as she had got its neck nicely straightened out, and was going to give the hedgehog a blow with its head, it *would* twist itself round and look up into her face, with such a puzzled expression that she could not help bursting out laughing: and when she had got its head down, and was going to begin again, it was very provoking to find that the hedgehog had unrolled itself, and was in the act of crawling away: besides all this, there was generally a ridge or a furrow in the way wherever she wanted to send the hedgehog to, and, as the doubled-up soldiers were always getting up and walking off to other parts of the ground, Alice soon came to the conclusion that it was a very difficult game indeed.

The players all played at once without waiting for turns, quarrelling all the while, and fighting for the hedgehogs; and in a very short time the Queen was in a furious passion, and went stamping about, and shouting, "Off with his head!" or "Off with her head!" about once in a minute.

Alice began to feel very uneasy: to be sure, she had not as yet had any dispute with the Queen, but she knew that it might happen any minute, "And then," thought she, "what would become of me? They're dreadfully fond of beheading people here: the great wonder is, that there's anyone left alive!"

She was looking about for some way of escape, and wondering whether she could get away without being seen, when she noticed a curious appearance in the air: it puzzled her very much at first, but after watching it a minute or two she made it out to be a grin, and she said to herself, "It's the Cheshire Cat: now I shall have somebody to talk to."

"How are you getting on?" said the Cat, as soon as there was mouth enough for it to speak with.

Alice waited till the eyes appeared, and then nodded. "It's no use speaking to it," she thought, "till its ears have come, or at least one of them." In another minute the whole head appeared, and then Alice put down her flamingo, and began an account of the game, feeling very glad she had someone to listen to her. The Cat seemed to think that there was enough of it now in sight, and no more of it appeared.

"I don't think they play at all fairly," Alice began, in rather a complaining tone, "and they all quarrel so dreadfully one can't hear one's-self speak—and they don't seem to have any rules in particular; at least, if there are, nobody attends to them—and you've no idea how confusing it is all the things being alive; for instance, there's the arch I've got to go through next walking about at the other end of the ground—and I should have croqueted the Queen's hedgehog just now, only it ran away when it saw mine coming!"

"How do you like the Queen?" said the Cat in a low voice.

"Not at all," said Alice; "she's so extremely—" Just then she noticed that the Queen was close behind her, listening: so she went on, "—likely to win, that it's hardly worthwhile finishing the game."

The Queen smiled and passed on.

"Who *are* you talking to?" said the King, coming up to Alice, and looking at the Cat's head with great curiosity.

"It's a friend of mine—a Cheshire Cat," said Alice: "allow me to introduce it."

"I don't like the look of it at all," said the King: "however, it may kiss my hand if it likes."

"I'd rather not," the Cat remarked.

"Don't be impertinent," said the King, "and don't look at me like that!" He got behind Alice as he spoke.

"A cat may look at a king," said Alice. "I've read that in some book, but I don't remember where."

"Well, it must be removed," said the King very decidedly, and he called to the Queen, who was passing at the moment, "My dear! I wish you would have this cat removed!"

The Queen had only one way of settling all difficulties, great or small. "Off with his head!" she said without even looking round.

"I'll fetch the executioner myself," said the King eagerly, and he hurried off.

Alice thought she might as well go back and see how the game was going on, as she heard the Queen's voice in the distance, screaming with passion. She had already heard her sentence three of the players to be executed for having missed their turns, and she did not like the look of things at all, as the game was in such confusion that she never knew whether it was her turn or not. So she went off in search of her hedgehog.

The hedgehog was engaged in a fight with another hedgehog, which seemed to Alice an excellent opportunity for croqueting one of them with the other: the only difficulty was, that her flamingo was gone across to the other side of the garden, where Alice could see it trying in a helpless sort of way to fly up into a tree.

By the time she had caught the flamingo and brought it back, the fight was over, and both the hedgehogs were out of sight. "But it doesn't matter much," thought Alice, "as all the arches are gone from this side of the ground." So she tucked it away under her arm, that it might not escape again, and went back to have a little more conversation with her friend.

When she got back to the Cheshire Cat, she was surprised to find quite a large crowd collected round it: there was a dispute going on between the executioner, the King, and the Queen, who were all talking at once, while all the rest were quite silent, and looked very uncomfortable.

The moment Alice appeared, she was appealed to by all three to settle the question, and they repeated their arguments to her, though, as they all spoke at once, she found it very hard to make out exactly what they said.

The executioner's argument was, that you couldn't cut off a head unless there was a body to cut it off from: that he had never had to do such a thing before, and he wasn't going to begin at *his* time of life. The King's argument was, that anything that had a head could be beheaded, and that you weren't to talk nonsense.

The Queen's argument was, that if something wasn't done about it in less than no time she'd have everybody executed, all round. (It was this last remark that had made the whole party look so grave and anxious.)

Alice could think of nothing else to say but, "It belongs to the Duchess: you'd better ask *her* about it."

"She's in prison," the Queen said to the executioner: "fetch her here." And the executioner went off like an arrow.

The Cat's head began fading away the moment he was gone, and, by the time he had come back with the Duchess, it had entirely disappeared; so the King and the executioner ran wildly up and down looking for it, while the rest of the party went back to the game.

CHAPTERS IX AND X

The Duchess returns and converses very agreeably with Alice. Meanwhile, the croquet-game comes to an end because the Queen, having quarrelled with all the players except Alice, has given orders for them to lose their heads. The Queen decides that Alice must meet two more occupants of Wonderland and takes her to meet a bossy Gryphon and a very unhappy Mock Turtle. (A "Mock Turtle," according to the Queen, is "the thing Mock Turtle Soup is made from." There is, of course, no such animal; mock or imitation turtle soup is made from beef instead of turtle meat. A Gryphon is another imaginary animal— half eagle and half lion.) Once the Queen leaves, the King pardons everyone who was sentenced to execution.

The Gryphon and Mock Turtle tell Alice what going to school under the sea is like, sing her songs, and dance a Lobster Quadrille. Then, the Gryphon hurries Alice off to attend a trial.

CHAPTER XI

WHO STOLE THE TARTS?

The King and Queen of Hearts were seated on their throne when they arrived, with a great crowd assembled about them—all sorts of little birds and beasts, as well as the whole pack of cards: the Knave was standing before them, in chains, with a soldier on each side to guard him; and near the King was the White Rabbit, with a trumpet in one hand, and a scroll of parchment in the other. In the very middle of the court was a table, with a large dish of tarts upon it: they looked so good, that it made Alice quite hungry to look at them—"I wish they'd get the trial done," she thought, "and hand round the refreshments!" But there seemed to be no chance of this, so she began looking at everything about her to pass away the time.

Alice had never been in a court of justice before, but she had read about them in books, and she was quite pleased to find that she knew the name of nearly everything there. "That's the judge," she said to herself, "because of his great wig."

The judge, by the way, was the King, and as he wore his crown over the wig (look at the frontispiece if you want to see how he did it), he did not look at all comfortable, and it was certainly not becoming.

"And that's the jury-box," thought Alice, "and those twelve creatures" (she was obliged to say "creatures," you see, because some of them were animals, and some were birds), "I suppose they are the jurors." She said this last word two or three times over to herself, being rather proud of it: for she thought, and rightly too, that very few little girls of her age knew the meaning of it at all. However, "jurymen" would have done just as well.

The twelve jurors were all writing very busily on slates. "What are they doing?" Alice whispered to the Gryphon. "They can't have anything to put down yet, before the trial's begun."

"They're putting down their names," the Gryphon whispered in reply, "for fear they should forget them before the end of the trial."

"Stupid things!" Alice began in a loud indignant voice, but she stopped herself hastily, for the White Rabbit cried out, "Silence in the court!" and the King put on his spectacles and looked anxiously round, to make out who was talking.

Alice could see, as well as if she were looking over their shoulders, that all the jurors were writing down "stupid things!" on their slates, and she could even make out that one of them didn't know how to spell "stupid," and that he had to ask his neighbour to tell him. "A nice muddle their slates'll be in before the trial's over!" thought Alice.

One of the jurors had a pencil that squeaked. This, of course, Alice could *not* stand, and she went round the court and got behind him, and very soon found an opportunity of taking it away. She did it so quickly that the poor little juror (it was Bill, the Lizard) could not make out at all what had become of it; so, after hunting all about for it, he was obliged to write with one finger for the rest of the day, and this was of very little use, as it left no mark on the slate.

"Herald, read the accusation!" said the King.

On this the White Rabbit blew three blasts on the trumpet, and then unrolled the parchment scroll, and read as follows:

> *"The Queen of Hearts, she made some tarts,*
> *All on a summer day:*
> *The Knave of Hearts, he stole those tarts,*
> *And took them quite away!"*

"Consider your verdict," the King said to the jury.

"Not yet, not yet!" the Rabbit hastily interrupted. "There's a great deal to come before that!"

"Call the first witness," said the King; and the White Rabbit blew three blasts on the trumpet, and called out, "First witness!"

The first witness was the Hatter. He came in with a teacup in one hand, and a piece of bread-and-butter in the other. "I beg pardon, your Majesty," he began, "for bringing these in: but I hadn't quite finished my tea when I was sent for."

"You ought to have finished," said the King. "When did you begin?"

The Hatter looked at the March Hare, who had followed him into the court, arm-in-arm with the Dormouse. "Fourteenth of March, I *think* it was," he said.

"Fifteenth," said the March Hare.

"Sixteenth," added the Dormouse.

"Write that down," the King said to the jury, and the jury eagerly wrote down all three dates on their slates, and then added them up, and reduced the answer to shillings and pence.

"Take off your hat," the King said to the Hatter.

"It isn't mine," said the Hatter.

"*Stolen!*" the King exclaimed, turning to the jury, who instantly made a memorandum of the fact.

"I keep them to sell," the Hatter added as an

explanation: "I've none of my own. I'm a Hatter."

Here the Queen put on her spectacles, and began staring hard at the Hatter, who turned pale and fidgeted.

"Give your evidence," said the King; "and don't be nervous, or I'll have you executed on the spot."

This did not seem to encourage the witness at all: he kept shifting from one foot to the other, looking uneasily at the Queen, and in his confusion he bit a large piece out of his teacup instead of the bread-and-butter.

Just at this moment Alice felt a very curious sensation, which puzzled her a good deal until she made out what it was: she was beginning to grow larger again, and she thought at first she would get up and leave the court; but on second thoughts she decided to remain where she was as long as there was room for her.

"I wish you wouldn't squeeze so," said the Dormouse, who was sitting next to her. "I can hardly breathe."

"I can't help it," said Alice very meekly: "I'm growing."

"You've no right to grow *here*," said the Dormouse.

"Don't talk nonsense," said Alice more boldly: "you know you're growing too."

"Yes, but *I* grow at a reasonable pace," said the Dormouse: "not in that ridiculous fashion." And he got up very sulkily and crossed over to the other side of the court.

All this time the Queen had never left off staring at the Hatter, and, just as the Dormouse crossed the court, she said to one of the officers of the court, "Bring me the list of the singers in the last concert!" on which the wretched Hatter trembled so, that he shook both his shoes off.

"Give your evidence," the King repeated angrily, "or I'll have you executed, whether you're nervous or not."

"I'm a poor man, your Majesty," the Hatter began in a trembling voice, "and I hadn't but just begun my tea—not above a week or so—and what with the bread-and-butter getting so thin—and the twinkling of the tea—"

"The twinkling of *what*?" said the King.

"It *began* with the tea," the Hatter replied.

"Of course, twinkling begins with a T!" said the King sharply. "Do you take me for a dunce? Go on!"

"I'm a poor man," the Hatter went on, "and most things twinkled after that—only the March Hare said—"

"I didn't!" the March Hare interrupted in a great hurry.

"You did!" said the Hatter.

"I deny it!" said the March Hare.

"He denies it," said the King: "leave out that part."

"Well, at any rate, the Dormouse said—" the Hatter went on, looking anxiously round to see if he would deny it too: but the Dormouse denied nothing, being fast asleep.

"After that," continued the Hatter, "I cut some more bread-and-butter—"

"But what did the Dormouse say?" one of the jury asked.

"That I can't remember," said the Hatter.

"You *must* remember," remarked the King, "or I'll have you executed."

The miserable Hatter dropped his teacup and bread-and-butter, and went down on one knee. "I'm a poor man, your Majesty," he began.

"You're a *very* poor *speaker*," said the King.

Here one of the guinea-pigs cheered, and was immediately suppressed by the officers of the court. (As that is rather a hard word, I will just explain to you how it was done. They had a large canvas bag, which tied up at the mouth with strings: into this they slipped the guinea-pig, head first, and then sat upon it.)

"I'm glad I've seen that done," thought Alice. "I've so often read in the newspapers, at the end of trials,

'There was some attempt at applause, which was immediately suppressed by the officers of the court,' and I never understood what it meant till now."

"If that's all you know about it, you may stand down," continued the King.

"I can't go no lower," said the Hatter: "I'm on the floor, as it is."

"Then you may *sit* down," the King replied.

Here the other guinea-pig cheered, and was suppressed.

"Come, that finishes the guinea-pigs!" thought Alice. "Now we shall get on better."

"I'd rather finish my tea," said the Hatter, with an anxious look at the Queen, who was reading the list of singers.

"You may go," said the King, and the Hatter hurriedly left the court, without even waiting to put his shoes on.

"—and just take his head off outside," the Queen added to one of the officers; but the Hatter was out of sight before the officer could get to the door.

"Call the next witness!" said the King.

The next witness was the Duchess' cook. She carried the pepper-box in her hand, and Alice guessed who it was, even before she got into the court, by the way the people near the door began sneezing all at once.

"Give your evidence," said the King.

"Shan't," said the cook.

The King looked anxiously at the White Rabbit, who said in a low voice, "Your Majesty must cross-examine *this* witness."

"Well, if I must, I must," the King said with a melancholy air, and, after folding his arms and frowning at the cook till his eyes were nearly out of sight, he said in a deep voice, "What are tarts made of?"

"Pepper, mostly," said the cook.

"Treacle," said a sleepy voice behind her.

"Collar that Dormouse!" the Queen shrieked out. Behead that Dormouse! Turn that Dormouse out of court! Suppress him! Pinch him! Off with his whiskers!"

For some minutes the whole court was in confusion, getting the Dormouse turned out, and, by the time they had settled down again, the cook had disappeared.

"Never mind!" said the King, with an air of great relief. "Call the next witness." And he added in an under-tone to the Queen, "Really, my dear, *you* must cross-examine the next witness. It quite makes my forehead ache!"

Alice watched the White Rabbit as he fumbled over the list, feeling very curious to see what the next witness would be like, "—for they haven't got much evidence *yet*," she said to herself. Imagine her surprise, when the White Rabbit read out, at the top of his shrill little voice, the name "Alice!"

CHAPTER XII

ALICE'S EVIDENCE

"Here!" cried Alice, quite forgetting in the flurry of the moment how large she had grown in the last few minutes, and she jumped up in such a hurry that she tipped over the jury-box with the edge of her skirt, upsetting all the jury-men onto the heads of the crowd below, and there they lay sprawling about, reminding her very much of a globe of gold-fish she had accidentally upset the week before.

"Oh, I *beg* your pardon!" she exclaimed in a tone of great dismay, and began picking them up again as quickly as she could, for the accident of the gold-fish

kept running in her head, and she had a vague sort of idea that they must be collected at once and put back into the jury-box, or they would die.

"The trial cannot proceed," said the King in a very grave voice, "until all the jurymen are back in their proper places—*all,*" he repeated with great emphasis, looking hard at Alice as he said so.

Alice looked at the jury-box, and saw that, in her haste, she had put the Lizard in head downwards, and the poor little thing was waving its tail about in a melancholy way, being quite unable to move. She soon got it out again, and put it right; "not that it signifies much," she said to herself; "I should think it would be *quite* as much use in the trial one way up as the other."

As soon as the jury had a little recovered from the shock of being upset, and their slates and pencils had been found and handed back to them, they set to work very diligently to write out a history of the accident, all except the Lizard, who seemed too much overcome to do anything but sit with its mouth open, gazing up into the roof of the court.

"What do you know about this business?" the King said to Alice.

"Nothing," said Alice.

"Nothing *whatever*?" persisted the King.

"Nothing whatever," said Alice.

"That's very important," the King said, turning to the jury. They were just beginning to write this down on their slates, when the White Rabbit interrupted. "*Un*important, your Majesty means, of course," he said in a very respectful tone, but frowning and making faces at him as he spoke.

"*Un*important, of course, I meant," the King hastily said, and went on to himself in an under-tone, "important—unimportant—unimportant—important—" as if he were trying which word sounded best.

Some of the jury wrote it down "important" and some "unimportant." Alice could see this, as she was near enough to look over their slates; "But it doesn't matter a bit," she thought to herself.

At this moment the King, who had been for some time busily writing in his note-book, called out "Silence!" and read out from his book, "Rule Forty-two. *All persons more than a mile high to leave the court.*"

Everybody looked at Alice.

"*I'm* not a mile high," said Alice.

"You are," said the King.

"Nearly two miles high," added the Queen.

"Well, I shan't go, at any rate," said Alice; "besides, that's not a regular rule: you invented it just now."

"It's the oldest rule in the book," said the King.

"Then it ought to be Number One," said Alice.

The King turned pale, and shut his note-book hastily. "Consider your verdict," he said to the jury, in a low trembling voice.

"There's more evidence to come yet, please your Majesty," said the White Rabbit, jumping up in a great hurry; "this paper has just been picked up."

"What's in it?" said the Queen.

"I haven't opened it yet," said the White Rabbit, "but it seems to be a letter, written by the prisoner to—to somebody."

"It must have been that," said the King, "unless it was written to nobody, which isn't usual, you know."

"Who is it directed to?" said one of the jurymen.

"It isn't directed at all," said the White Rabbit; "in fact, there's nothing written on the *outside*." He unfolded the paper as he spoke, and added, "It isn't a letter after all: it's a set of verses."

"Are they in the prisoner's handwriting?" asked another of the jurymen.

"No, they're not," said the White Rabbit, "and that's the queerest thing about it." (The jury all looked puzzled.)

"He must have imitated somebody else's hand," said the King. (The jury all brightened up again.)

"Please your Majesty," said the Knave, "I didn't write it, and they can't prove I did: there's no name signed at the end."

"If you didn't sign it," said the King, "that only makes the matter worse. You *must* have meant some mischief, or else you'd have signed your name like an honest man."

There was a general clapping of hands at this: it was the first really clever thing the King had said that day.

"That *proves* his guilt," said the Queen.

"It proves nothing of the sort!" said Alice. "Why, you don't even know what they're about!"

"Read them," said the King.

The White Rabbit put on his spectacles. "Where shall I begin, please your Majesty?" he asked.

"Begin at the beginning," the King said, gravely, "and go on till you come to the end: then stop."
These were the verses the White Rabbit read:

"They told me you had been to her,
And mentioned me to him:
She gave me a good character,
But said I could not swim.

He sent them word I had not gone
(We know it to be true):
If she should push the matter on,
What would become of you?

I gave her one, they gave him two,
You gave us three or more;
They all returned from him to you,
Though they were mine before.

If I or she should chance to be
Involved in this affair,
He trusts to you to set them free,
Exactly as we were.

My notion was that you had been
(Before she had this fit)
An obstacle that came between
Him, and ourselves, and it.

239

Don't let him know she liked them best,
For this must ever be
A secret, kept from all the rest,
Between yourself and me."

"That's the most important piece of evidence we've heard yet," said the King, rubbing his hands; "so now let the jury—"

"If any one of them can explain it," said Alice (she had grown so large in the last few minutes that she wasn't a bit afraid of interrupting him), "I'll give him sixpence. *I* don't believe there's an atom of meaning in it."

The jury all wrote down on their slates, "*She* doesn't believe there's an atom of meaning in it," but none of them attempted to explain the paper.

"If there's no meaning in it," said the King, "that saves a world of trouble, you know, as we needn't try to find any. And yet I don't know," he went on, spreading out the verses on his knee, and looking at them with one eye; "I seem to see some meaning in them, after all. '—*said I could not swim*—' you can't swim, can you?" he added, turning to the Knave.

The Knave shook his head sadly. "Do I look like it?" he said. (Which he certainly did *not*, being made entirely of cardboard.)

"All right, so far," said the King, and he went on muttering over the verses to himself: " '*We know it to*

240

be true'—that's the jury, of course—*'I gave her one,
they gave him two—'* why, that must be what he did
with the tarts, you know—"

"But it goes on, *'They all returned from him to you,'*"
said Alice.

"Why, there they are!" said the King triumphantly,
pointing to the tarts on the table. "Nothing can be
clearer than *that*. Then again—*'before she had this fit—'*
you never had fits, my dear, I think?" he said to
the Queen.

"Never!" said the Queen
furiously, throwing an
inkstand at the Lizard as she
spoke. (The unfortunate
little Bill had left off writing
on his slate with one finger,
as he found it made no
mark; but he now hastily
began again, using the ink,
that was trickling down his
face, as long as it lasted.)

"Then the words don't *fit* you," said the King, looking round the court with a smile. There was a dead silence.

"It's a pun!" the King added in an angry tone, and everybody laughed. "Let the jury consider their verdict," the King said, for about the twentieth time that day.

"No, no!" said the Queen. "Sentence first—verdict afterwards."

"Stuff and nonsense!" said Alice loudly. "The idea of having the sentence first!"

"Hold your tongue!" said the Queen, turning purple.

"I won't!" said Alice.

"Off with her head!" the Queen shouted at the top of her voice. Nobody moved.

"Who cares for you?" said Alice (she had grown to her full size by this time). "You're nothing but a pack of cards!"

At this the whole pack rose up into the air, and came flying down upon her; she gave a little scream, half of fright and half of anger, and tried to beat them off, and found herself lying on the bank, with her head in the lap of her sister, who was gently brushing away some dead leaves that had fluttered down from the trees onto her face.

"Wake up, Alice dear!" said her sister; "why, what a long sleep you've had!"

"Oh, I've had such a curious dream!" said Alice, and she told her sister, as well as she could remember them, all these strange Adventures of hers that you have just been reading about; and when she had finished, her sister kissed her, and said, "It *was* a curious dream, dear, certainly: but now run in to your tea; it's getting late." So Alice got up and ran off, thinking while she ran, as well she might, what a wonderful dream it had been.

ACKNOWLEDGMENTS

All possible care has been taken to trace ownership and secure permission for each selection in this series. The Great Books Foundation wishes to thank the following authors, publishers, and representatives for permission to reprint copyrighted material:

Thank You, M'am, from THE LANGSTON HUGHES READER. Copyright 1958 by Langston Hughes; renewed 1986 by George Houston Bass. Reprinted by permission of Harold Ober Associates, Inc.

THE STORY OF WANG LI, by Elizabeth Coatsworth. Copyright 1932 by Elizabeth Coatsworth. Reprinted by permission of Mark Paterson and Associates, on behalf of The Estate of Elizabeth Coatsworth.

Cedric, from TALES FROM MOOMINVALLEY, by Tove Jansson. Translation copyright 1963 by Ernest Benn Limited. Reprinted by permission of A & C Black (Publishers) Limited.

Fresh, from WHAT THE NEIGHBOURS DID AND OTHER STORIES, by Philippa Pearce. Copyright 1959, 1967, 1969, 1972 by Philippa Pearce. Reprinted by permission of Penguin Books Limited.

THE ENCHANTED STICKS, by Steven J. Myers. Copyright 1979 by Steven J. Myers. Reprinted by permission of Coward, McCann & Geoghegan.

Mr. Singer's Nicknames, from MY GREAT-GRANDFATHER AND I, by James Krüss. Translation copyright 1964 by Atheneum Publishers. Reprinted by permission of Atheneum Publishers, an imprint of Macmillan Publishing Company.

ILLUSTRATION CREDITS

Brock Cole prepared the illustration for *Mr. Singer's Nicknames.*

Diane Cole prepared the illustrations for *The Water-Horse of Barra* and *Vasilissa the Beautiful.*

David Cunningham prepared the illustration for *Thank You, M'am.*

Donna Diamond's illustration for *The Enchanted Sticks* is from the book of the same name. Illustration copyright 1979 by Donna Diamond. Reprinted by permission of Coward, McCann & Geoghegan.

Tove Jansson's illustrations for *Cedric* are from TALES FROM MOOMINVALLEY. Illustrations copyright 1962 by Tove Jansson. Her illustrations on pages 80 and 81 are from COMET IN MOOMINLAND, by Tove Jansson. Illustrations copyright 1946 by Tove Jansson. Reprinted by permission of A & C Black (Publishers) Limited.

Rudyard Kipling's illustration for *The Elephant's Child* is from JUST SO STORIES, by Rudyard Kipling, first published in 1902.

Emily Arnold McCully prepared the illustration for *Fresh.*

Howard Pyle's illustration for *Wisdom's Wages and Folly's Pay* is from TWILIGHT LAND, by Howard Pyle, first published in 1895.

John Tenniel's illustrations for *Alice's Adventures in Wonderland* are from the book by Lewis Carroll, first published in 1865 by Macmillan.

Ed Young prepared the illustration for *The Story of Wang Li.*

Cover art by Ed Young. Copyright 1992 by Ed Young.

Text and cover design by William Seabright, William Seabright & Associates.